California

Everyday Mathematics®

CALIFORNIA

The University of Chicago School Mathematics Project

Student Math Journal
Volume 1

Grade 1

McGraw Hill | Wright Group

The McGraw·Hill Companies

The University of Chicago School Mathematics Project (UCSMP)

Max Bell, Director, UCSMP Elementary Materials Component; Director, *Everyday Mathematics* First Edition
James McBride, Director, *Everyday Mathematics* Second Edition
Andy Isaacs, Director, *Everyday Mathematics* Third Edition
Amy Dillard, Associate Director, *Everyday Mathematics* Third Edition

Authors

Max Bell	Robert Hartfield	Kathleen Pitvorec	Amy Dillard
Jean Bell	Andy Isaacs	Peter Saecker	Rachel Malpass McCall*
John Bretzlauf	James McBride		*Third Edition only*

Technical Art
Diana Barrie

Teachers in Residence
Jeanine O'Nan Brownell
Andrea Cocke
Brooke A. North

Editorial Assistant
Rossita Fernando

Contributors

Robert Balfanz, Judith Busse, Mary Ellen Dairyko, Lynn Evans, James Flanders, Dorothy Freedman, Nancy Guile Goodsell, Pam Guastafeste, Nancy Hanvey, Murray Hozinsky, Deborah Arron Leslie, Sue Lindsley, Mariana Mardrus, Carol Montag, Elizabeth Moore, Kate Morrison, William D. Pattison, Joan Pederson, Brenda Penix, June Ploen, Herb Price, Dannette Riehle, Ellen Ryan, Marie Schilling, Susan Sherrill, Patricia Smith, Robert Strang, Jaronda Strong, Kevin Sweeney, Sally Vongsathorn, Esther Weiss, Francine Williams, Michael Wilson, Izaak Wirzup

Photo Credits

©C Squared Studios/Getty Images, p.34; ©Ralph A. Clevenger/CORBIS, cover, *center;* Getty Images, cover, *bottom left;* ©Tom and Dee Ann McCarthy/CORBIS, cover, *right;* ©Shutterstock International, p.24; ©Stockdisc/Getty Images, p.31.

California *Everyday Mathematics* Reviewers

Dr. Dale Oliver, Humboldt State University
Dr. Bill Jacobs, University of California, Santa Barbara

Dr. Elizabeth Burroughs, Humboldt State University
Dr. Alfred Manaster, University of California, San Diego

---

www.WrightGroup.com

 **Wright Group**

Copyright © 2008 by Wright Group/McGraw-Hill.

Printed in the United States of America.

Send all inquiries to:
Wright Group/McGraw-Hill
P.O. Box 812960
Chicago, IL 60681

ISBN   978-0-07-609787-6
MHID   0-07-609787-0

3 4 5 6 7 8 9 CPC 13 12 11 10 09 08

Contents

UNIT 3 Visual Patterns, Number Patterns, and Counting

UNIT 4 · Measurement and Basic Facts

Activity Sheets

Koala
19 lb

Cheetah
120 lb

Penguin
75 lb

LESSON 1·4   Number Writing: 1

Draw a picture of 1 thing.

1	
$1 + 0$	•
$/$ $2 - 1$	
uno	one

LESSON 1·4   Number Writing: 2

Draw a picture of 2 things.

2	
$1 + 1$	• •
$//$ $3 - 1$	
dos	two

Number Writing: 3

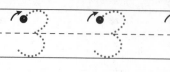

Draw a picture of 3 things.

3	
///	2 + 1 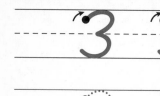
	4 − 1
tres	three

Number Writing: 4

(1) (2)

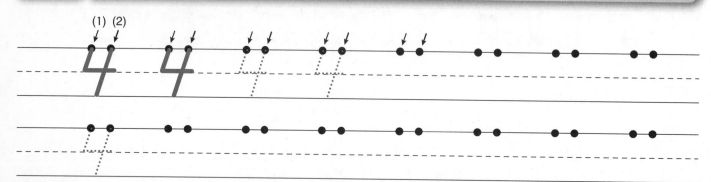

Draw a picture of 4 things.

4	
////	3 + 1
	5 − 1
cuatro	four

Number Sense **1.1**

Dice-Roll and Tally

Roll a die. Use tally marks to record the results
on this chart.

	Tallies	Total

LESSON 1·9

Calendar

Month _____

Sunday	Monday	Tuesday	Wednesday	Thursday	Friday	Saturday

Number Sense **1.1**, 1.0; Measurement and Geometry 1.2

LESSON 1·9 · Number Writing: 5

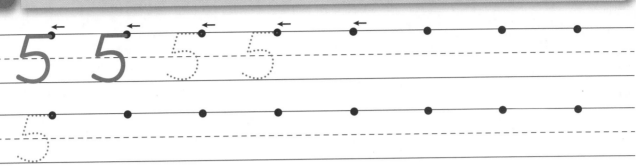

5

4 + 1

~~HHT~~ 6 − 1

cinco   five

Draw a picture of 5 things.

LESSON 1·9 · Number Writing: 6

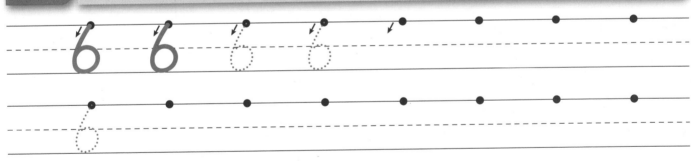

6

5 + 1

~~HHT~~ / 7 − 1

seis   six

Draw a picture of 6 things.

A Thermometer

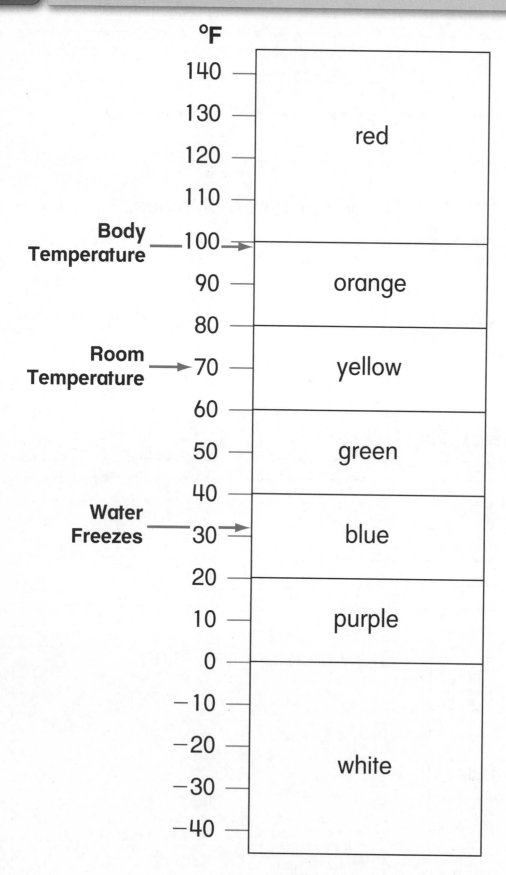

Rolling for 50

Materials

◆ a die

◆ a marker for each player

◆ a gameboard

Players 2

Skill Count by 1s

Object of the Game

To be the first player to reach 50

Roll	Spaces
1	3 up
2	2 back
3	5 up
4	6 back
5	8 up
6	10 up

Directions

Take turns.

1. Put your marker on 0.

2. Roll the die. Look in the table to see how many spaces to move.

3. The first player to reach 50 wins.

| 0 |

| 1 | 2 | 3 | 4 | 5 | 6 | 7 | 8 | 9 | 10 |

| 11 | 12 | 13 | 14 | 15 | 16 | 17 | 18 | 19 | 20 |

| 21 | 22 | 23 | 24 | 25 | 26 | 27 | 28 | 29 | 30 |

| 31 | 32 | 33 | 34 | 35 | 36 | 37 | 38 | 39 | 40 |

| 41 | 42 | 43 | 44 | 45 | 46 | 47 | 48 | 49 | 50 |

LESSON 2·2 Information about Me

My first name is _____.

My second name is _____.

My last name is _____.

I am _____ years old.

Put candles on your cake.

My area code and home telephone number are

(_____ _____ _____) _____ _____ _____ – _____ _____ _____ _____

   (area code)   (telephone number)

Important Phone Numbers

Emergency number: _____ _____ _____

School number:

(_____ _____ _____) _____ _____ _____ – _____ _____ _____ _____

Local library number:

(_____ _____ _____) _____ _____ _____ – _____ _____ _____ _____

Date _____

Number Writing: 7

7   7   7   7

7

7	
6 + 1	
~~HHT~~ //	8 − 1
siete	seven

Draw a picture of 7 things.

Number Writing: 8

8   8   8   8   8

8

8	
7 + 1	
~~HHT~~ ///	9 − 1
ocho	eight

Draw a picture of 8 things.

Math Boxes

1. Count up by 1s.

7,   8,   9,

_____ , _____ , _____ ,

_____ , _____ , _____ ,

_____ , _____

2. Count up by 5s.

0,   5,   10,

_____ , _____ , _____ ,

_____ , _____ , _____

3. Write the number that comes before.

_____ 19

_____ 23

_____ 31

_____ 36

4. Write the number.

_____   _____

LESSON 2·4 — Number Writing: 9

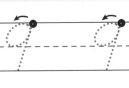

9 9 *9* *9*

9

  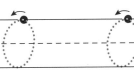

9	
8 + 1	
‖‖‖ ‖‖‖	10 − 1
nueve	nine

Draw a picture of 9 things.

LESSON 2·4 — Number Writing: 0

0 0 O O

O

0	
0 + 0	☐
1 − 1	
cero	zero

Math Boxes

1. How many tally marks?

₤₤₤ ₤₤₤ //

Choose the best answer.

- ⬭ 3
- ⬭ 12
- ⬭ 15
- ⬭ 10

2. Draw the shape you are more likely to grab from the bag.

_____

3. Make a sum of 10 pennies.

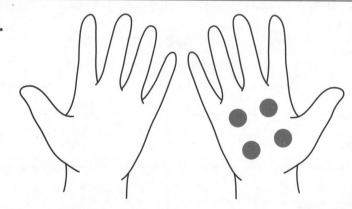

4. Complete the number line.

8   9   ___ ___ ___ ___ ___

1) NS 1.0   2) SDAP 1.0   3) NS 1.3
4) NS **1.1**

Date _____

1. Count back by 1s.

     18,   *17,*   *16,*

_____, _____, _____,

_____, _____, _____,

_____, _____

2. Count up by 5s.

     10,   *15,*   *20,*

_____, _____, _____,

_____, _____

3. What number comes before 10?

Choose the best answer.

 1

◯ 0

◯ 9

◯ 11

4. Write the number.

_____   _____

LESSON 2·6   **Telling Time**

1. Record the time.

_____ o'clock

_____ o'clock

_____ o'clock

_____ o'clock

2. Draw the hour hand.

2 o'clock

6 o'clock

Measurement and Geometry 1.2

Date _____

1. How many tally marks?

~~HHT~~ ~~HHT~~ ~~HHT~~ IIII

_____ tally marks

2. Draw the shape you are more likely to grab from the bag.

_____

3. Make a sum of 10 pennies.

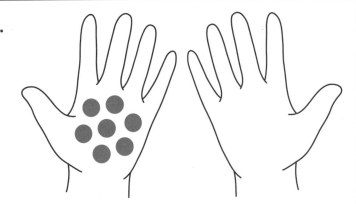

4. Complete the number line.

22   23   ____ ____   ____   ____   ____

LESSON 2·7 **Math Boxes**

1. Record the time.

_____ o'clock

2. Use your number grid.

Start at 12.

Count up 5.

You end at _____.

3. Circle the winning card in *Top-It*.

11   9

4. What day of the week is today?

_____

What day of the month?

_____

What day of school?

_____

1) MG 1.2   2) NS 2.0   3) NS 1.2
4) MG 1.2

Date _____

1. Use your number grid.

Start at 11.

Count back 6.

You end at _____.

2. How much money?

Ⓟ Ⓟ Ⓟ Ⓟ Ⓟ Ⓟ

_____ ¢

3. What comes next?

    _____

Choose the best answer.

 △

 □

 ◯

 ◇

4. Count up by 2s.

0,   2,   4, _____, _____, _____,

_____, _____, _____, _____, _____

Exploring Pennies and Nickels

Write the total amount. Then show the amount using fewer coins.
Write ⓟ for penny and ⓝ for nickel.

(*Hint:* Exchange pennies for nickels.)

1. ⓟ ⓟ ⓟ ⓟ ⓟ ⓟ ⓟ   _____¢

Show this amount using fewer coins.

2. ⓟ ⓟ ⓟ ⓟ ⓟ ⓟ ⓟ ⓟ ⓟ   _____¢

Show this amount using fewer coins.

3. ⓟ ⓟ ⓟ ⓟ ⓟ ⓟ ⓟ ⓟ ⓟ ⓟ ⓟ ⓟ   _____¢

Show this amount using fewer coins.

Try This

4. ⓝ ⓟ ⓟ ⓟ ⓟ ⓟ ⓟ   _____¢

Show this amount using fewer coins.

Number Sense 1.5, **2.4**; Mathematical Reasoning 2.0

Date

1. Record the time.

_____ o'clock

2. Use your number grid.

Start at 15.

Count up 9.

You end at _____.

Choose the best answer.

⬭ 6

⬭ 15

⬭ 24

⬭ 23

3. Circle the winning card in _Top-It_.

| 19 | 9 |

4. What day of the week is today?

_____

What day of the month?

_____

What day of school?

_____

LESSON 2·10 Counting Pennies and Nickels

Write the total amount.

1.

_____ ¢

2.

_____ ¢

3.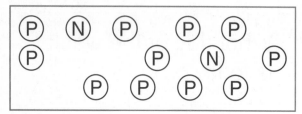

_____ ¢

Try This

4.

P	N	P	P	P
P		P	N	P
	P	P	P	P

Write the total amount. _____ ¢

Show this amount using fewer coins.

Number Sense 1.5; Number Sense 2.4

Date _____

---

1. Use your number grid.

Start at 18.

Count back 8.

You end at _____.

2. How much money?

Ⓟ Ⓟ Ⓟ Ⓟ Ⓟ Ⓟ Ⓟ Ⓟ

Choose the best answer.

⬭ 10¢

⬭ 8¢

⬭ 16¢

⬭ 9¢

---

3. Draw what comes next.

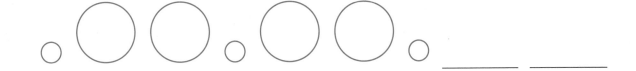

---

4. Count up by 2s.

2,   4,   6,   _____, _____,

_____, _____, _____, _____, _____

Math Boxes

1. How much money?

Ⓝ Ⓝ Ⓟ

_____ ¢

2. Draw the hour hand.

2 o'clock

3.

The Pets We Own	
Pet	Tallies
Cat	~~HHH~~ ~~HHH~~
Dog	~~HHH~~ ///
Other	~~HHH~~ /

How many cats? _____ cats

How many dogs?

_____ dogs

4. Count up by 10s.

20,   30,   40,

_____, _____, _____,

_____, _____, _____,

_____, _____

Date _____

1. Use your number grid.

Start at 23.

Count up 8.

You end at _____.

2. How much money?

N N P P P

_____ ¢

3. Draw what comes next.

 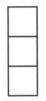

_____ _____

_____ _____

4. Count up by 2s.

6,   8,   10,   _____,

_____, _____, _____, _____

LESSON 2·13 School Store Mini-Poster 1

crayon
9¢

scissors
10¢

ball
25¢

toy truck
5¢

pencil
18¢

jacks
1¢

eraser
7¢

Number Sense 1.0, 1.5, 2.0, **2.5**; Algebra and Functions 1.0, 1.1, 1.2

Date _____

1. Tell how much money.

_____¢

_____¢

How much money in all? _____¢

2. Buy 2 items from the School Store. Draw them below.

3. Under each item you drew, show how much it costs.
Use Ⓟ for pennies and Ⓝ for nickels.

4. Circle the item that costs more.
How much more does it cost? _____¢

Try This

5. Draw 2 items that cost a total of 14¢.

Math Boxes

1. Use Ⓟ and Ⓝ to show the cost.

28¢

_____

2. It is _____ o'clock.

Choose the best answer.

- ⬭ 12
- ⬭ 8
- ⬭ 6
- ⬭ 7

3. Fill in the table.

The Pets We Own		
Pet	**Tallies**	**Total**
Cat	⊮ ⁄⁄⁄	
Dog	⊮ ⊮ ⁄⁄	
Other	⊮ ⁄⁄⁄⁄	

4. Count back by 10s.

90,   80,   70, _____, _____, _____,

_____, _____, _____

LESSON
2·14   **Math Boxes**

---

1. Write the number.

_____   _____

2. Count up by 10s.

30,   40,   _____,

_____, _____, _____,

_____, _____

---

3. Use your template. Make a pattern with ◯s and △s.

---

4. Complete the number line.

_____   10   11   _____ _____ _____ _____

LESSON 3·1 Patterns

1. Draw the next 2 shapes.
Use your Pattern-Block Template.

    ___ ___

    ___ ___

     ___ ___

2. Make up your own pattern.
Then ask your partner to draw the next 2 shapes.

Try This

3. Draw the next 3 shapes.

Statistics, Data Analysis, and Probability **2.1**; Mathematical Reasoning 3.0

Date _____

1. Circle the winning card in *Top-It*.

| 18 | 17 |

2. Draw the hour hand.

6 o'clock

3. Record the total amount.

(P) (P) (P) (P) (P) (P)

_____ ¢

Use (P) and (N) to show this amount with fewer coins.

4. What is the temperature?

Fill in the circle next to the best answer.

Ⓐ about 60°F

Ⓑ about 40°F

Ⓒ about 70°F

Ⓓ about 50°F

°F
60—
50—
40—
30—
20—
10—

LESSON 3·2 Odd and Even Patterns

How many 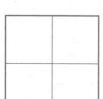s? Label **odd** or **even**.

Example:

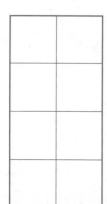

$\underline{\quad 4 \quad}$

$\underline{\quad even \quad}$

1.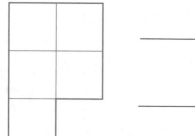

_____

_____

2.

_____

_____

3.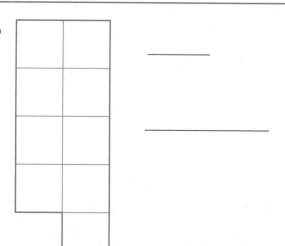

_____

_____

How many ☆s? Label **odd** or **even**.

4.

_____ _____

Try This

5.

_____

_____

Number Sense 1.0, **1.1**; Statistics, Data Analysis, and Probability **2.1**

Date _____

1. Use Ⓟ and Ⓝ to show the cost.

18¢

2. What shape comes next?

Fill in the circle next to the best answer.

Ⓐ 　　Ⓑ ▢

Ⓒ 　　Ⓓ ◯

3. Make sums of 10 pennies.

Left Hand	Right Hand
9	1
4	
	5

4. Complete this part of the number grid.

1	2			5
		13	14	
21				25
	32		34	

LESSON 3·3

The 2s Pattern

									0
1	2	3	4	5	6	7	8	9	10
11	12	13	14	15	16	17	18	19	20
21	22	23	24	25	26	27	28	29	30
31	32	33	34	35	36	37	38	39	40
41	42	43	44	45	46	47	48	49	50
51	52	53	54	55	56	57	58	59	60
61	62	63	64	65	66	67	68	69	70
71	72	73	74	75	76	77	78	79	80
81	82	83	84	85	86	87	88	89	90
91	92	93	94	95	96	97	98	99	100
101	102	103	104	105	106	107	108	109	110

Shade the 2s pattern on the above grid.

Fill in the missing numbers below.

___0___, ___2___, ___4___, _____, ___8___, _____,

_____, __14__, _____, _____, __20__, _____,

_____, _____, __28__, _____, _____, __34__

Number Sense **1.1**, **2.4**; Statistics, Data Analysis, and Probability **2.1**

Date _____

1. Circle the winning card in *Top-It.*

22   18

2. Draw the hour hand.

4 o'clock

3. Record the total amount.

Ⓝ Ⓝ Ⓟ Ⓟ Ⓟ Ⓟ Ⓟ

_____¢

Use Ⓝ to show this amount with fewer coins.

4. Color the thermometer to show about 40°F.

°F
50—
40—
30—
20—
10—

LESSON 3·4 Math Boxes

1. Use Ⓟ and Ⓝ to show the cost.

25¢

2. Draw what comes next.

■ □ ■ □ ____ ____

○ ◎ ○ ◎ ____ ____

3. Make sums of 10 pennies.

Left Hand	Right Hand
3	7
4	
	8

4. Complete this part of the number grid.

		8		10
	17			
	27	28	29	
36				

LESSON 3·5   Number-Line Skip Counting

1. Show counts by 2s.

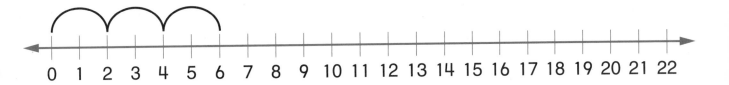

2. Show counts by 5s.

3. Show counts by 10s.

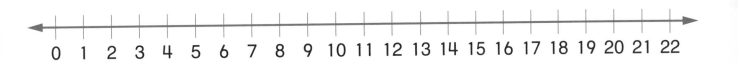

Try This

4. Show counts by 3s.

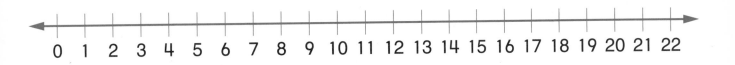

Date _____

1.

Favorite Colors	
Red	‖‖‖ ‖‖‖
Green	‖‖‖ ‖‖‖ ‖‖
Yellow	‖‖‖ ‖‖‖
Blue	‖‖‖ ‖‖‖ ‖‖‖

Which color is most popular?

Fill in the circle next to the best answer.

Ⓐ red   Ⓒ yellow

Ⓑ green   Ⓓ blue

2. Count by 5s. Circle your counts on the number grid.

1	2	3	4	5	6	7	8	9	10
11	12	13	14	15	16	17	18	19	20
21	22	23	24	25	26	27	28	29	30
31	32	33	34	35	36	37	38	39	40
41	42	43	44	45	46	47	48	49	50

3. How many ☐ s? _____

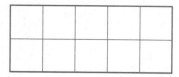

Odd or even? _____

4. Complete the number line.

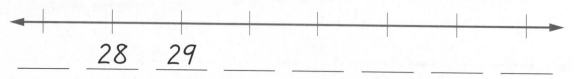

_____ 28   29 _____ _____ _____ _____ _____

1) SDAP 1.2   2) NS 2.4   3) NS 1.0
4) NS 1.1

LESSON 3·6 Adding and Subtracting on the Number Line

A vertical number line marked 0 through 25.

1. Start at 6. Count up 2 hops. Where do you end up?

6 + 2 = _____

2. Start at 4. Count up 9 hops. Where do you end up?

4 + 9 = _____

3. Start at 15. Count back 7 hops. Where do you end up?

15 − 7 = _____

4. Start at 18. Count back 8 hops. Where do you end up?

18 − 8 = _____

Try This

5. 5 + 8 = _____

6. 11 − 8 = _____

7. 3 + 13 = _____

LESSON 3·6 Math Boxes

1. Complete the table.

Before	Number	After
11	12	13
	8	
	15	
	19	

2. How many days are in a week?

Fill in the circle next to the best answer.

(A) 5

(B) 7

(C) 10

(D) 30

3. Count up by 2s.

12,   14,   16,

———, ———, ———,

———, ———, ———,

———, ———

4. Circle the longer one.

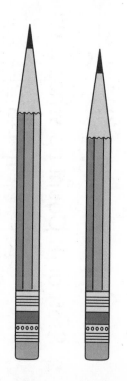

1) NS 2.3
4) MG 1.1
2) MG 1.2
3) NS 2.4

LESSON 3·7 **Telling Time**

1. Record the time.

half-past _____ o'clock   half-past _____ o'clock

_____ o'clock   _____ o'clock

2. Draw the hour hand and the minute hand.

half-past 1 o'clock   7 o'clock

LESSON 3·7 Math Boxes

1.

Weather	
Sunny	∦∦∦ ∦∦∦ ∦∦∦ ///
Cloudy	∦∦∦ ∦∦∦ ////
Rainy	∦∦∦ ∦∦∦
Snowy	∦∦∦ ////

How many sunny days?

_____ sunny days

Were there more rainy days or snowy days?

more _____ days

2. Count up by 5s.

___15___ , ___20___ , ___25___ , _____ , _____ , _____ ,

_____ , _____ , _____

3. How many ☐s?   _____

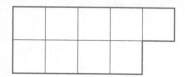

Odd or even? _____

4. Make sums of 10 pennies.

Left Hand	Right Hand
2	8
5	
	9

1) SDAP 1.2   2) NS 2.4   3) NS 1.0
4) NS 1.3

Date _____

←|—|—|—|—|—|—|—|—|—|—|—|—|—|—|—|—|—|—|—|—|—|—|—|—|—|→
0 1 2 3 4 5 6 7 8 9 10 11 12 13 14 15 16 17 18 19 20 21 22 23 24 25

1.

| **Rule**
Count up by 2s |

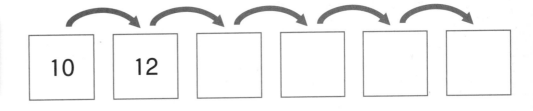

10 12 ☐ ☐ ☐ ☐

2.

| **Rule**
Add 5 |

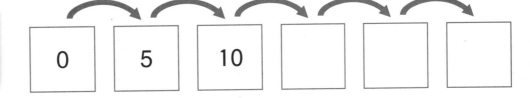

0 5 10 ☐ ☐ ☐

3.

| **Rule**
Count back by 2s |

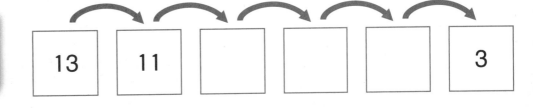

13 11 ☐ ☐ ☐ 3

4.

| **Rule**
Subtract 3 |

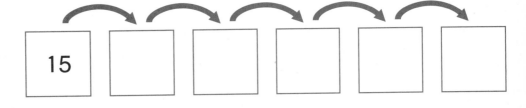

15 ☐ ☐ ☐ ☐ ☐

LESSON 3·8   **Math Boxes**

---

1. Complete the table.

Before	Number	After
7	8	9
	10	
	20	
	29	

2. What month is it?

_____

How many days are in this month?

_____ days

---

3. Count back by 2s.

20,   18,   16,

_____, _____, _____,

_____, _____, _____,

_____, _____

4. Circle the longer one.

CRAYON

CRAYON

---

1) NS 2.3   2) MG 1.2   3) NS 2.4
4) MG 1.1

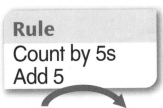 **LESSON 3·9** **More Frames and Arrows**

1. Fill in the frames.

Rule
Count by 5s
Add 5

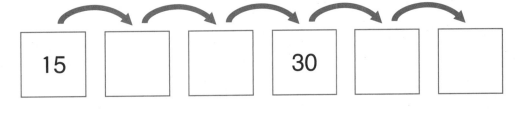

| 15 | | | 30 | | |

2. Fill in the rule.

Rule

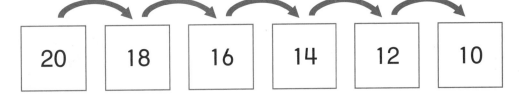

| 20 | 18 | 16 | 14 | 12 | 10 |

3. Fill in the rule and the frames.

Rule

| 7 | 10 | 13 | | | |

4. Fill in the rule and the frames.

Rule

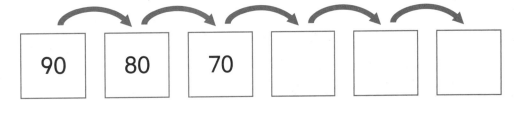

| 90 | 80 | 70 | | | |

5. Make up your own.

Rule

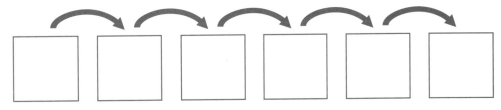

LESSON 3·9 **Math Boxes**

---

1. Use your number line.

Start at 0.

Count up 6.

You end at _____.

$0 + 6 =$ _____

---

2. Record the time.

half-past _____ o'clock

3.

Rule

Count by 5s

| 15 | | | | |

---

4. Fill in the blanks.

_10_, _20_, _30_, ____, _50_,

____, ____, _80_, ____, ____

---

1) NS 2.1   2) MG 1.2   3)SDAP 2.1
4) NS 2.4

Date _____

1. Odd or even?

_____   _____

_____   _____

2. Make sums of 10 pennies.

Left Hand	Right Hand
7	3
4	
	8

3. Use a calculator. Count up by 3s.

0,   3,   6,

_____ , _____ , _____ ,

_____ , _____ , _____ ,

_____ , _____

4. What is the number model?

Fill in the circle next to the best answer.

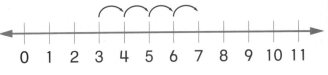

0 1 2 3 4 5 6 7 8 9 10 11

(A) $3 + 5 = 7$

(B) $4 + 3 = 7$

(C) $3 - 4 = 7$

(D) $3 + 4 = 7$

LESSON
3·11   **Coin Exchange**

Show each amount using fewer coins.
Write Ⓟ for penny, Ⓝ for nickel, and Ⓓ for dime.

1.

2.

3.

4.

Number Sense 1.5, Number Sense 2.4

Date _____

1. Use your number line.
Start at 3.
Count up 5.
You end at _____.

Fill in the circle next to the best answer.

Ⓐ 3

Ⓑ 5

Ⓒ 7

Ⓓ 8

2. What time is it?

half-past _____ o'clock

3. Fill in the rule and the missing numbers.

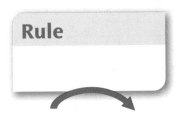

| 5 | 10 | | | |

4. Count up by 10s.

__20__ , __30__ , __40__ , _____ , _____ ,

_____ , _____ , _____ , _____ , _____

LESSON 3·12 How Much Money?

How much money?
Use your coins.

Example:

<u> 35 </u> ¢

Ⓟ	Ⓝ	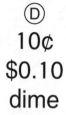 Ⓓ
1¢	5¢	10¢
$0.01	$0.05	$0.10
penny	nickel	dime

How much money? Use your coins.

1.   _____ ¢

2.   _____ ¢

3.

    _____ ¢

Try This

4. Ⓓ Ⓓ Ⓝ Ⓝ Ⓝ Ⓟ Ⓟ _____ ¢

Number Sense 1.5, Number Sense 2.4

1. Use your number line.
Start at 8.
Count back 5.

You end at _____.

8 − 5 = _____

2. Draw the hour hand and
the minute hand.

half-past 12 o'clock

3. How much money?

Ⓓ Ⓓ Ⓓ Ⓝ Ⓟ Ⓟ

Fill in the circle next to the
best answer.

Ⓐ 6¢

Ⓑ 22¢

Ⓒ 30¢

Ⓓ 37¢

4. Write the number model.

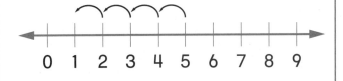

0 1 2 3 4 5 6 7 8 9

_____

LESSON 3·13 Math Boxes

1. Odd or even?

_____   _____

2. Make sums of 10 pennies.

Left Hand	Right Hand
8	2
6	
	3

3. Use a calculator.
Count up by 7s.

0,   7,   14,

_____, _____, _____,

_____, _____, _____,

_____, _____

4. Write the number model.

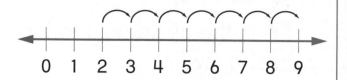

0 1 2 3 4 5 6 7 8 9

_____

1) NS 1.0   2) NS 1.3   3) SDAP 2.1
4) AF 1.0

LESSON 3·14 Domino Parts and Totals

Write 3 numbers for each domino.

Example:

Total	
6	
Part	Part
4	2

1.

Total	
Part	Part

2.

Total	
Part	Part

3.

Total	
Part	Part

4.

Total	
Part	Part

5.

Total	
Part	Part

---

6. Draw dots in the domino. Write 3 numbers in the diagram.

Total	
Part	Part

Try This

7. Find the missing part. Draw dots in the domino.

Total	
8	
Part	Part
3	

Math Boxes

1. Use your number line.
Start at 6.
Count back 4.

You end at _____.

$6 - 4 =$ _____

2. Draw the hour hand and the minute hand.

half-past 2 o'clock

3. Write the total amount.

Ⓓ Ⓓ Ⓝ Ⓝ Ⓝ Ⓝ Ⓟ Ⓟ

_____ ¢

4. Write the number model.

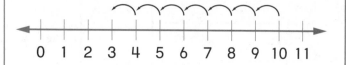

0 1 2 3 4 5 6 7 8 9 10 11

_____

1) NS 2.1   2) MG 1.2   3) NS 1.5
4) AF 1.1

Date _____

1. Color the thermometer to show about 75°F.

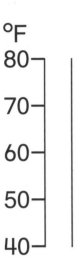

°F
80—
70—
60—
50—
40—

2. Circle the longer one.

3. Complete this part of the number grid.

1	2			5
11	12			15
		23		25
			34	

4. Count up by 10s.

_50_ , _60_ ,

_70_ , _____ ,

_____ , _____ ,

_____ , _____ ,

_____ , _____

LESSON 4·1

Reading Thermometers

°F

120 —
110 —
Body Temperature → 100 —
90 —
80 —
Room Temperature → 70 —
60 —
50 —
40 —
Water Freezes → 30 —
20 —
10 —
0 —
−10 —
−20 —
−30 —
−40 —

Write the °F temperatures.

1.
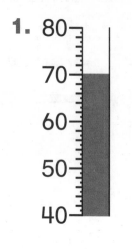

2.
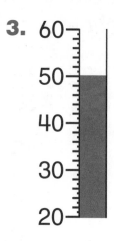

3.

4.
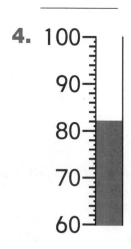

5.
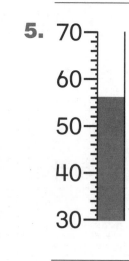

6.
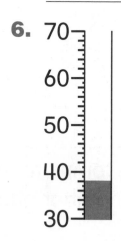

Color to show each temperature.

7. 80°F

8. 62°F

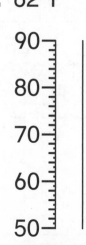

9. 58°F

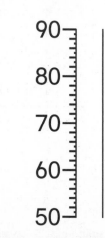

Measurement and Geometry 1.0

LESSON 4·1 **Math Boxes**

---

1. What is the temperature today?

_____ °F

Is the temperature odd or even?

_____

---

2. Write the missing numbers.

| Rule −4 |

| 24 | 20 | | 12 | |

---

3. Draw and solve.

Olga had 6 pennies.

Tyson gave her 2 more pennies.

How many pennies does Olga have now?

_____ pennies

---

4. Circle the winning domino in *Domino Top-It*.

LESSON 4·2 My Body and Units of Measure

Measure some objects. Record your measurements.

Unit	Picture	Object	Measurements
digit			about _____ digits
yard			about _____ yards
hand			about _____ hands
pace			about _____ paces
cubit			about _____ cubits
arm span (or fathom)			about _____ arm spans
foot			about _____ feet
hand span			about _____ hand spans

Measurement and Geometry 1.0; Statistics, Data Analysis, and Probability 2.1

My Height   57

Things that are taller than I am

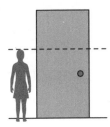

Things that are about the same size as I am

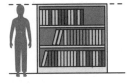

Things that are shorter than I am

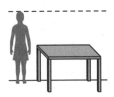

LESSON 4·2

Subtracting on a Number Grid

-9	-8	-7	-6	-5	-4	-3	-2	-1	0
1	2	3	4	5	6	7	8	9	10
11	12	13	14	15	16	17	18	19	20
21	22	23	24	25	26	27	28	29	30
31	32	33	34	35	36	37	38	39	40
41	42	43	44	45	46	47	48	49	50
51	52	53	54	55	56	57	58	59	60
61	62	63	64	65	66	67	68	69	70

1. Start at 38. Count back 4. Where do you end up? _____

$38 - 4 =$ _____

2. Start at 59. Count back 9. Where do you end up? _____

$59 - 9 =$ _____

3. Start at 62. Count back 11. Where do you end up? _____

$62 - 11 =$ _____

4. Start at 70. Count back 17. Where do you end up? _____

$70 - 17 =$ _____

Try This

Subtract.

5. $43 - 20 =$ _____   **6.** $35 - 15 =$ _____

Number Sense **2.5**, **2.4**, 2.6

Math Boxes

---

1. What is the temperature?
Fill in the circle next to the best answer.

○ **A.** 70°F

○ **B.** 72°F

○ **C.** 80°F

○ **D.** 76°F

°F

---

2. Draw the missing shape.

---

3. Complete the table.

Before	Number	After
24	25	26
	29	
	33	
	37	
	40	

4. Use a number grid.
Count by 10s.

8,   18, _____, _____,

_____, _____, _____, _____,

_____, _____, _____

LESSON 4·3   My Foot and the Standard Foot

Measure two objects with the cutout of your foot.
Draw pictures of the objects or write their names.

1. I measured

It is about _____ _____ feet.
(your name)

2. I measured

It is about _____ _____ feet.
(your name)

Measure the same two objects with the foot-long foot.
Sometimes it is called the *standard foot.*

3. I measured

It is about _____ feet.

4. I measured

It is about _____ feet.

Measurement and Geometry 1.0

LESSON 4·3   **Math Boxes**

---

1. What is the temperature today?

_____ °F

Is the temperature odd or even?

_____

---

2. What comes next?

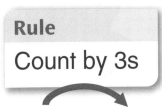

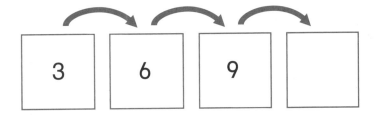

Fill in the circle next to the best answer.

○ **A.** 10   ○ **B.** 11   ○ **C.** 12   ○ **D.** 6

---

3. Draw and solve.

Ava had 9 pennies.

She lost 4 pennies.

How many pennies does Ava have now?

_____ pennies

4. Circle the winning domino in *Domino Top-It.*

LESSON 4•4

Inches

Pick 4 short objects to measure. Draw or name them.
Then measure the objects with your ruler.

1.

About ______ inches long

2.

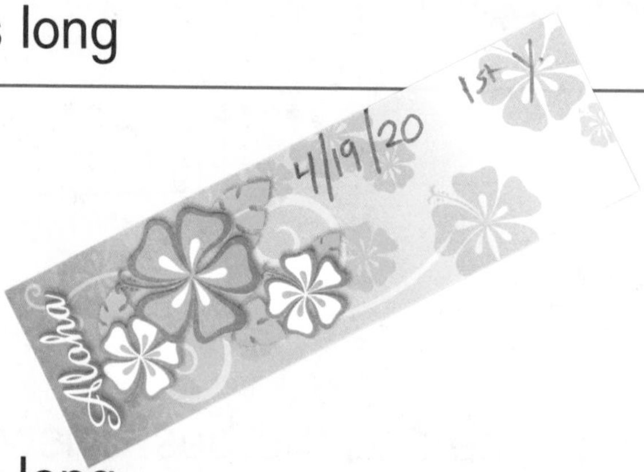

About ______ inches long

3.

About ______ inches long

4.

About ______ inches long

Measurement and Geometry 1.0

LESSON 4·4 Math Boxes

1. Record the temperatures.

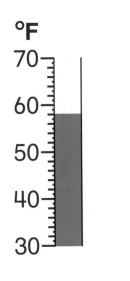

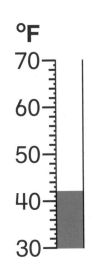

_____°F   _____°F

2. Draw the missing shape.

 _____

3. Complete the table.

Before	Number	After
27	28	29
	35	
	50	
	101	

4. Use a number grid.
Count by 10s.

/ ,   / / , _____, _____,

_____, _____, _____, _____,

_____, _____, _____

Measuring in Inches

1. Choose two objects to measure. Estimate each object's length. Measure the objects to the nearest inch.

Object (Name it or draw it.)	My Estimate	My Measurement
	about _____ inches	about _____ inches
	about _____ inches	about _____ inches

Measure each line segment.

2. _____

    H/19/20

    about _____ inches

3. _____

    about _____ inches

4. _____

    about _____ inches

5. _____

    about _____ inches

Draw a line segment about

6. 4 inches long.

7. 2 inches long.

Measurement and Geometry 1.0

LESSON 4·5

Math Boxes

---

1. Measure your calculator.

It is about _____ inches long.

---

2. Favorite Pets, Mr. Lee's Class

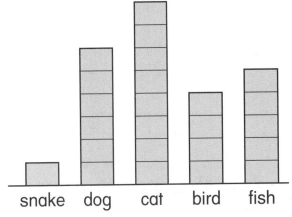

| snake | dog | cat | bird | fish |

What is the most popular

pet? _____

How many children like

snakes? _____

---

3. Count back by 5s.

40, 35, 30, _____,

_____, _____, _____, _____,

_____

---

4. Write the sums.

⚀ + ⚂ = _____

⚁ + ⚄ = _____

⚃ + ⚃ = _____

LESSON 4·6 Measuring Parts of the Body

Record your wrist size below.

1. Wrist  It is about _____ inches.

Measure these othe_____ of your body. Work with a partner.

2. Elbow  It is about _____ inches.

3. Ankle 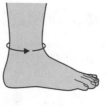 It is about _____ inches.

4. Head 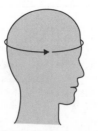 It is about _____ inches.

5. Hand span It is about _____ inches.

Measurement and Geometry 1.0

LESSON 4·6 Domino Parts and Totals

Find the totals.

Example:

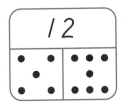

12
⦁ ⦁ ｜ ⦁ ⦁ ⦁

1.

2.

3.

4.	Total	
	Part	Part
	7	4

5.	Total	
	Part	Part
	2	9

6.	Total	
	Part	Part
	6	3

7.	Total	
	Part	Part
	8	8

8.	Total	
	Part	Part
	7	7

9.	Total	
	Part	Part
	8	3

Try This

Find the missing parts.

10.	Total	
	12	
	Part	Part
	6	

11.	Total	
	14	
	Part	Part
		5

12.	Total	
	15	
	Part	Part
		7

Number Sense 1.3

LESSON 4·6 **Math Boxes**

1. Draw a line segment about 3 inches long.

2. Which coins show 26¢?

Fill in the circle next to the best answer.

○ **A.** Ⓝ Ⓝ Ⓟ Ⓟ Ⓟ Ⓟ Ⓟ Ⓟ

○ **B.** Ⓓ Ⓓ Ⓟ

○ **C.** Ⓓ Ⓝ Ⓝ Ⓟ

○ **D.** Ⓓ Ⓓ Ⓝ Ⓟ

3. Use your number line.

Start at 4.

Count up 5 hops.

You end at _____.

$4 + 5 =$ _____

4. Tom has Ⓝ Ⓟ Ⓟ Ⓟ.

Bill has Ⓓ.

Who has more money?

_____

How much more money?

_____ ¢

1) MG 1.0   2) NS 1.5   3) NS 2.5
4) NS 1.5

LESSON 4·7 Measuring Height

1. Today's date is _____.

   My height is _____ inches.

2. This is a bar graph. It shows the heights of children in my class.

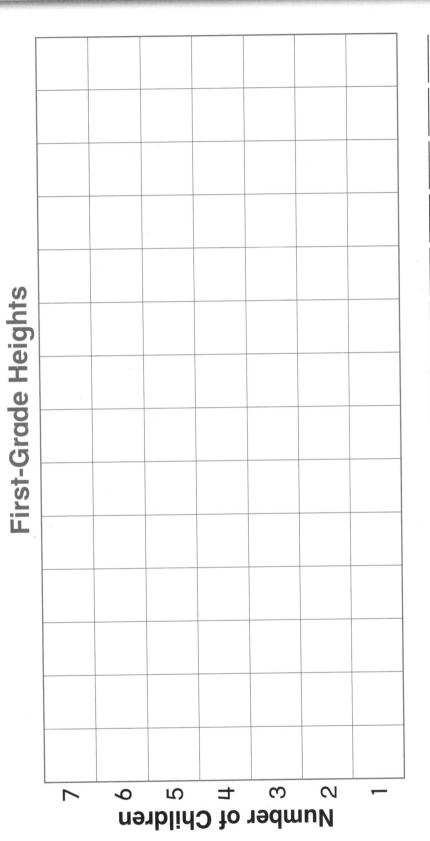

First-Grade Heights

Number of Children: 7 6 5 4 3 2 1

Inches Tall

3. The "typical" height for first graders in my class is about _____ inches.

1. How long is the line segment?

_____

Fill in the circle next to the best answer.

○ **A.** about 3 inches

○ **B.** about 2 inches

○ **C.** about 1 inch

○ **D.** about 4 inches

2. Favorite Drinks, Ms. Brown's Class

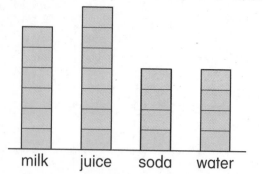

How many children like milk?

_____ children

Do more children like juice or soda?

_____

3. Count back by 2s.

36,   34,   32,

_____, _____, _____,

_____, _____, _____,

_____, _____, _____

4. Write the sums.

6 + 1 = _____

5 + 5 = _____

3 + 4 = _____

1) MG 1.0   2) SDAP 1.2   3) NS 2.4
4) AF 1.2

LESSON 4·8 # Telling Time

Record the time.

1.

_____ o'clock

2.

half-past _____ o'clock

3.

quarter-past _____ o'clock

4.

quarter-to _____ o'clock

Try This

Draw the hands to show the time.

5.

half-past 3 o'clock

6.

quarter-to 5 o'clock

LESSON 4·8 **Math Boxes**

1. Draw a line segment about 2 inches long.

2. Show 47¢.

Use Ⓓ, Ⓝ, and Ⓟ.

3. Use your number line.

Start at 6.

Count up 5 hops.

You end at _____.

6 + 5 = _____

4. Nico has Ⓓ Ⓓ Ⓟ.

Kenisha has Ⓓ Ⓝ Ⓝ.

Who has more money?

_____

How much more money?

_____ ¢

1) MG 1.0   2) NS 1.5   3) NS 2.5
4) NS 1.5

LESSON 4·9 School-Year Timeline

Think about these times of the year.
Draw pictures of things that happen during each of these months.

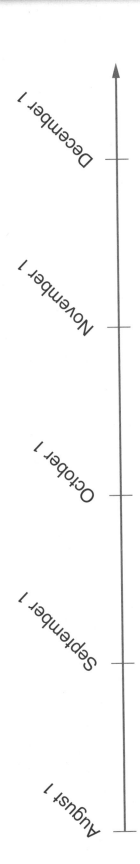

December 1

November 1

October 1

September 1

August 1

LESSON 4·9 Telling Time to the Quarter-Hour

Record the time.

1.

_____ o'clock

2.

half-past _____ o'clock

3.

quarter-after _____ o'clock

4.

quarter-after _____ o'clock

5.

quarter-to _____ o'clock

6.

quarter-to _____ o'clock

Measurement and Geometry 1.2

LESSON 4·9 **Math Boxes**

1. Measure your journal.

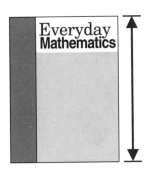

It is about _____ inches long.

2. What time is it?

Fill in the circle next to the best answer.

○ **A.** quarter-to 5 o'clock

○ **B.** quarter-to 4 o'clock

○ **C.** quarter-to 6 o'clock

○ **D.** quarter-to 9 o'clock

3. Use your number line.

Start at 8.

Count back 5 hops.

You end at _____.

8 − 5 = _____

4. Write the sums.

5 + 4 = _____

6 + 3 = _____

LESSON 4·10   Math Boxes

1. Are you more likely to grab black or white?

_____

2. Write the missing numbers.

Rule
Count by 2s

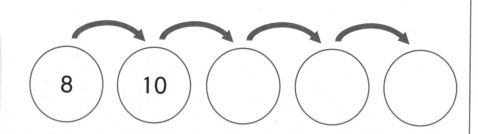

8   10   ◯   ◯   ◯

3. Record the time.

quarter-after _____ o'clock

4. Make sums of 9 pennies.

Left Hand	Right Hand
4	5
7	
	1

1) MR 2.0   2) SDAP 2.1   3) NS 2.1
4) AF 1.0

LESSON 4·11   **Domino Sums**

Draw a line from each domino to its matching numbers.
Then use the dominoes to find the sums.

1.

4 + 2 = _____

2.

3 + 1 = _____

3.

_____ = 1 + 5

4.

2 + 2 = _____

5.

_____ = 3 + 3

6.

_____ = 1 + 4

Try This

7. Draw dots to complete the domino. Write a fact to go with it.

_____ + _____ = _____

LESSON 4·11 Math Boxes

---

1. Measure the line segment.

_____

It is about _____ inches long.

---

2. What time is it?

quarter-to _____ o'clock

---

3. Use your number line.

Start at 9.

Count back 7 hops.

You end at _____.

$9 - 7 =$ _____

---

4. Write the sums.

$1 + 5 =$ _____ $6 + 6 =$ _____

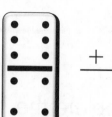

$\begin{array}{r} 6 \\ + 4 \\ \hline \end{array}$ $\begin{array}{r} 2 \\ + 3 \\ \hline \end{array}$

---

1) MG 1.0   2) MG 1.2   3) NS 2.1
4) AF 1.0

LESSON 4·12   Math Boxes

1. Are you more likely to grab black or white?

_____

2. What is the rule?

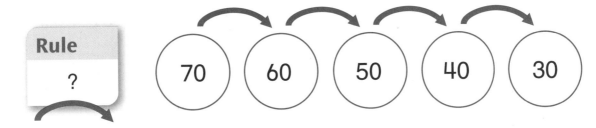

| Rule |
| ? |

70 60 50 40 30

Fill in the circle next to the best answer.

○ **A.** Count up by 2s

○ **B.** + 10

○ **C.** Subtract 5

○ **D.** − 10

3. Draw the hands.

quarter-to 6 o'clock

4. Make sums of 15 pennies.

Left Hand	Right Hand
10	5
8	
	6

LESSON 4·13 **Math Boxes**

---

1. Circle the winning domino in *Domino Top-It.*

---

2. Tim has 10¢.

Jan has 5¢.

Who has more money?

_____

How much more money?

_____ ¢

---

3. Write the sums.

 = _____

 + = _____

 + = _____

---

4. Make sums of 8 pennies.

Left Hand	Right Hand
3	5
4	
	8

---

1) NS 1.0 2) NS 2.5 3) AF 1.2
4) NS 1.3

Date _____

Tens-and-Ones Mat

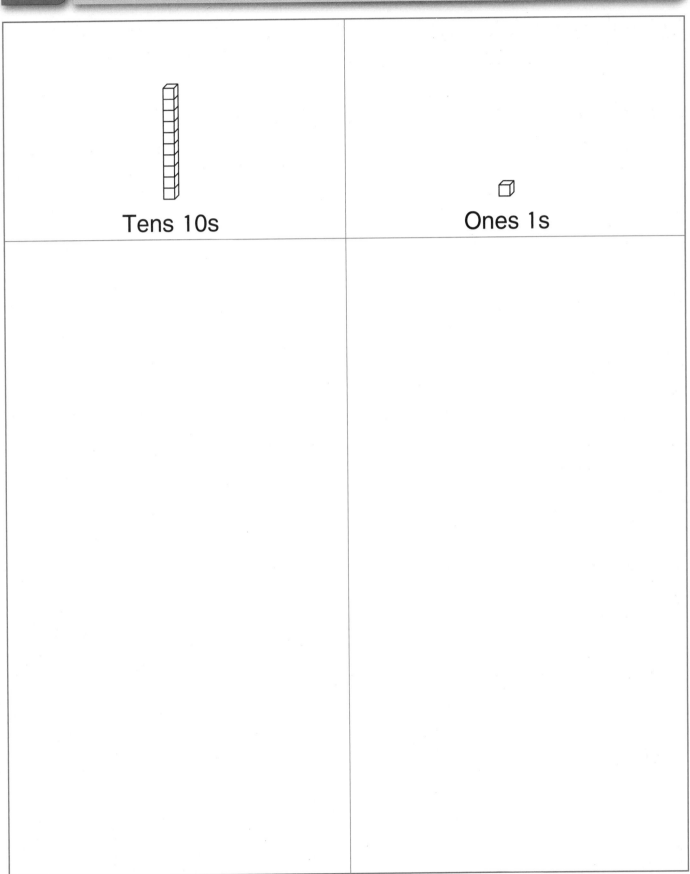

Tens 10s

Ones 1s

LESSON 5·1   Tens-and-Ones Riddles

Solve the riddles. Use your base-10 blocks to help you.

Example: 2 ▯ and 3 ▫   What am I? __23__

1. 6 ▯ and 5 ▫   What am I? _____

2. 7 ▯ and 2 ▫   What am I? _____

3. 6 longs and 4 cubes. What am I? _____

4. 7 longs and 0 cubes. What am I? _____

Try This

Trade to find the answers.

5. 1 long and 11 cubes. What am I? _____

6. 2 longs and 14 cubes. What am I? _____

7. Make up your own riddle.
Ask a friend to solve it.

Number Sense 1.4; Mathematical Reasoning 1.2

Date _____

1. Solve the riddles.

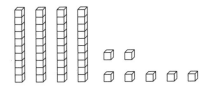

What am I? _____   What am I? _____

2. Fill in the rule and the missing numbers.

Rule

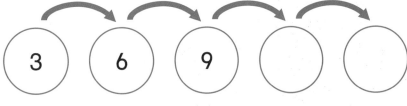

3   6   9   ◯   ◯

3. Find the sums.

$5 + 4 =$ _____

_____ $= 3 + 7$

4. How many tallies?

̶H̶H̶T̶ ̶H̶H̶T̶ ̶H̶H̶T̶ ///

_____ tallies

Odd or even?

_____

LESSON 5·2 Place-Value Mat

	Hundreds
	Tens
	Ones

Number Sense **1.2**; Number Sense 1.4

Date _____

1. Solve the riddles.

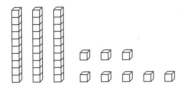

What am I? _____

What am I? _____

2. Make a tally for 14.

_____

3. Use your number grid.

Start at 45.

Count up 13.

You end at _____.

45 + 13 = _____

4. Draw and solve.

Trey has 5 cats and 2 dogs.

How many pets does Trey have?

_____ pets

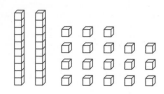

Math Boxes

LESSON 5·3

1. What am I?

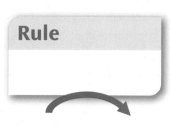

Choose the best answer.

◯ 20   ◯ 30

◯ 38   ◯ 218

2. Fill in the rule and the missing numbers.

Rule

(2) (12) (22) (   ) (   )

3. Find the sums.

_____ = 2 + 5

5 + 7 = _____

4. Write the number.

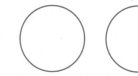

HHT HHT HHT HHT HHT HHT

HHT HHT //

_____

Odd or even?

_____

1) NS 1.4   2) SDAP 2.1   3) AF 1.0
4) NS 1.0

Date _____

---

1. Use | and • to show the number 42.

2. How many tallies?

HHT HHT HHT HHT ///

Choose the best answer.

◯ 19

◯ 23

◯ 25

◯ 43

---

3. Use your number grid.

Start at 48.

Count up 15.

You end at _____.

48 + 15 = _____

4. Draw and solve.

Rosa had 9 grapes.

She ate 3 grapes.

How many grapes does Rosa have left?

_____ grapes

LESSON 5·5 Math Boxes

---

1. Circle the tens place.

73   52   88   15   30

---

2. Write the number model.

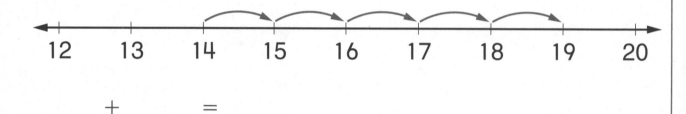

12   13   14   15   16   17   18   19   20

_____ + _____ = _____

---

3. Measure to the nearest inch.

_____

It is about _____ inches long.

_____

It is about _____ inches long.

---

4. Draw the missing dots.

Find the total number of dots.

6 + 4 = _____

7 + 3 = _____

---

1) NS 1.4   2) NS 2.6   3) MG 1.0
4) AF 1.1

LESSON 5·6 **"Less Than" and "More Than" Number Models**

Write < for "is less than" and > for "is more than."

1. 19 lb ◯ 23 lb

2. 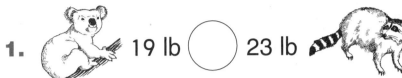 41 lb ◯ 14 lb

3.  75 lb ◯ 56 lb

4. 7 lb ◯ 6 lb

5.  50 lb ◯ 98 lb

LESSON 5·6 "Less Than" and "More Than" Number Models *(cont.)*

Try This

Write < for "is less than" and > for "is more than."

6. 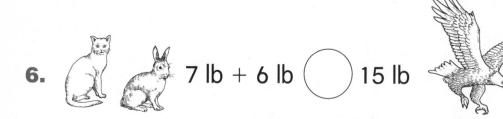 7 lb + 6 lb ◯ 15 lb

7. 120 lb ◯ 50 lb + 41 lb

8.  14 lb + 15 lb ◯ 23 lb

9. 75 lb ◯ 56 lb + 23 lb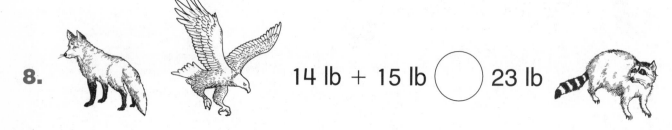

10. 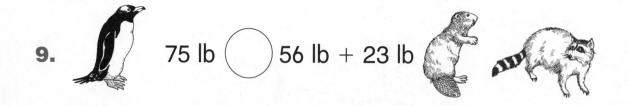 14 lb + 6 lb ◯ 19 lb

Number Sense 1.2

Date _____

---

1. Fill in the pattern.

○ ◉ ● ____ ◉ ● ○ ◉ ____

---

2. Show 32¢ with the fewest coins.

Use Ⓓ, Ⓝ, and Ⓟ.

---

3.   **Judy's Dice Rolls**

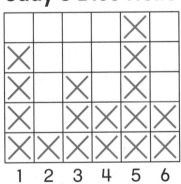

1 2 3 4 5 6
Number of Dots

How many times did Judy roll a 1?

_____ times

What number did Judy roll the most?

_____

---

4. Draw and solve.

The garden has 4 ladybugs and 9 ants.

How many insects are there in all?

_____ insects

LESSON 5·7 How Much More? How Much Less?

Find each difference.

1. John Ⓟ Ⓟ Ⓟ Ⓟ Ⓟ Ⓟ Ⓟ Ⓟ

Nick Ⓟ Ⓟ

Who has more? _____ How much more? _____ ¢

2. June Ⓟ Ⓟ Ⓟ Ⓟ Ⓟ Ⓟ Ⓟ Ⓟ Ⓟ

Mia Ⓟ Ⓟ Ⓟ Ⓟ Ⓟ Ⓟ

Who has less? _____ How much less? _____ ¢

3. Dante Ⓟ Ⓟ Ⓟ Ⓟ Ⓟ Ⓟ Ⓟ

Kala Ⓟ Ⓟ Ⓟ Ⓟ Ⓟ Ⓟ Ⓟ Ⓟ Ⓟ Ⓟ Ⓟ Ⓟ Ⓟ Ⓟ

Who has less? _____ How much less? _____ ¢

Try This

4. Carlos has 12 pennies.

Mary has 20 pennies.

Who has more? _____

How much more? _____ ¢

Number Sense 2.0, **2.5**, 2.6; Algebra and Functions 1.0, 1.2

Date _____

1. Circle the ones place.

12   40   6   77   54

2. Write the number model.

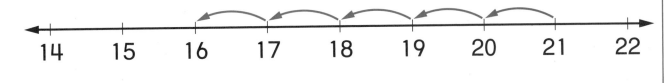

14   15   16   17   18   19   20   21   22

_____ − _____ = _____

3. How long is the line segment?

_____

Choose the best answer.

◯ about 2 inches

◯ about 3 inches

◯ about 4 inches

◯ about 5 inches

4. Draw the missing dots.

Find the total number of dots.

8 + 6 = _____

4 + 9 = _____

LESSON 5·8 Number Stories

Here is a number story Mandy made up.

I have 4 balloons.
Jamal brought 1 more.
We have 5 balloons together.

$4 + 1 = 5$

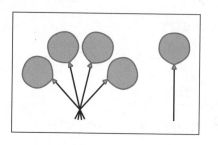

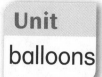

Unit
balloons

Record your own number story.
Fill in the unit box.
Write a number model.
You may want to draw a
picture for your story.

Unit

Number Sense **2.5**; Algebra and Functions 1.1, 1.2, 1.3

Date _____

---

1. Fill in the pattern.

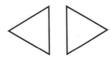

---

2. How much money?

Choose the best answer.

○ 71¢   ○ 61¢

○ 46¢   ○ 40¢

---

3.   **Teeth Lost**

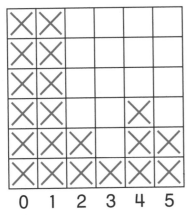

0 1 2 3 4 5
Number of Teeth

How many children have lost 0 teeth?

_____ children

How many children have lost more than 3 teeth?

_____ children

---

4. Draw and solve.

The chicken has 6 eggs.

2 eggs hatch.

How many eggs are left?

_____ eggs

LESSON 5·9 Dice-Throw Record

Roll a pair of dice. Draw an X in a box for the sum, from the bottom up. Which number reached the top first? _____

2	3	4	5	6	7	8	9	10	11	12

NS 1.3, **2.1**; SDAP 1.1; MR 3.0

Math Boxes

---

1. Write <, >, or =.

3 ☐ 13

17 ☐ 15

24 ☐ 42

28 ☐ 26

---

2. Draw and solve.

Meg has 8 pennies.

Maya has 3 pennies.

Who has more pennies?

_____

How many more pennies?

_____ pennies

---

3. How much money?

Ⓓ Ⓝ Ⓝ Ⓝ Ⓝ Ⓝ Ⓟ Ⓟ Ⓟ

_____¢

Show this amount with fewer coins.

Use Ⓟ, Ⓝ, and Ⓓ.

---

4. Draw the hands.

quarter-after 9 o'clock

Date _____

1 + 6 = ___	2 + 6 = ___	3 + 6 = ___	4 + 6 = ___	5 + 6 = ___	6 + 6 = ___
1 + 5 = ___	2 + 5 = ___	3 + 5 = ___	4 + 5 = ___	5 + 5 = ___	6 + 5 = ___
1 + 4 = ___	2 + 4 = ___	3 + 4 = ___	4 + 4 = ___	5 + 4 = ___	6 + 4 = ___
1 + 3 = ___	2 + 3 = ___	3 + 3 = ___	4 + 3 = ___	5 + 3 = ___	6 + 3 = ___
1 + 2 = ___	2 + 2 = ___	3 + 2 = ___	4 + 2 = ___	5 + 2 = ___	6 + 2 = ___
1 + 1 = ___	2 + 1 = ___	3 + 1 = ___	4 + 1 = ___	5 + 1 = ___	6 + 1 = ___

Number Sense **2.1** ; Number Sense 1.3

Date _____

1. Draw and solve.

Jade has 5 pennies.

Max has 9 pennies.

Who has fewer pennies?

_____

How many fewer pennies?

_____ fewer pennies

2. Write the sums.

⚃ + ⚄ = _____

_____ = ⚃ + ⚁

_____ = ⚀ + ⚂

3. Record the temperature.

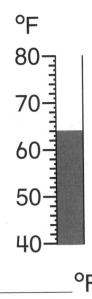

°F

_____ °F

4. Count up by 5s.

25, _____, _____,

_____, _____, _____,

_____, _____

LESSON 5·11 Facts Table

0 + 0 **0**	0 + 1 **1**	0 + 2 **2**	0 + 3 **3**	0 + 4 **4**	0 + 5 **5**	0 + 6 **6**	0 + 7 **7**	0 + 8 **8**	0 + 9 **9**	0 + 10 **10**
1 + 0 **1**	1 + 1 **2**	1 + 2 **3**	1 + 3 **4**	1 + 4 **5**	1 + 5 **6**	1 + 6 **7**	1 + 7 **8**	1 + 8 **9**	1 + 9 **10**	1 + 10 **11**
2 + 0 **2**	2 + 1 **3**	2 + 2 **4**	2 + 3 **5**	2 + 4 **6**	2 + 5 **7**	2 + 6 **8**	2 + 7 **9**	2 + 8 **10**	2 + 9 **1**	2 + 10 **12**
3 + 0 **3**	3 + 1 **4**	3 + 2 **5**	3 + 3 **6**	3 + 4 **7**	3 + 5 **8**	3 + 6 **9**	3 + 7 **10**	3 + 8 **11**	3 + 9 **12**	3 + 10 **13**
4 + 0 **4**	4 + 1 **5**	4 + 2 **6**	4 + 3 **7**	4 + 4 **8**	4 + 5 **9**	4 + 6 **10**	4 + 7 **11**	4 + 8 **12**	4 + 9 **13**	4 + 10 **14**
5 + 0 **5**	5 + 1 **6**	5 + 2 **7**	5 + 3 **8**	5 + 4 **9**	5 + 5 **10**	5 + 6 **11**	5 + 7 **12**	5 + 8 **13**	5 + 9 **14**	5 + 10 **15**
6 + 0 **6**	6 + 1 **7**	6 + 2 **8**	6 + 3 **9**	6 + 4 **10**	6 + 5 **11**	6 + 6 **12**	6 + 7 **13**	6 + 8 **14**	6 + 9 **15**	6 + 10 **16**
7 + 0 **7**	7 + 1 **8**	7 + 2 **9**	7 + 3 **10**	7 + 4 **11**	7 + 5 **12**	7 + 6 **13**	7 + 7 **14**	7 + 8 **15**	7 + 9 **16**	7 + 10 **17**
8 + 0 **8**	8 + 1 **9**	8 + 2 **10**	8 + 3 **11**	8 + 4 **12**	8 + 5 **13**	8 + 6 **14**	8 + 7 **15**	8 + 8 **16**	8 + 9 **17**	8 + 10 **18**
9 + 0 **9**	9 + 1 **10**	9 + 2 **11**	9 + 3 **12**	9 + 4 **13**	9 + 5 **14**	9 + 6 **15**	9 + 7 **16**	9 + 8 **17**	9 + 9 **18**	9 + 10 **19**
10 + 0 **10**	10 + 1 **11**	10 + 2 **12**	10 + 3 **13**	10 + 4 **14**	10 + 5 **15**	10 + 6 **16**	10 + 7 **17**	10 + 8 **18**	10 + 9 **19**	10 + 10 **20**

Number Sense **2.1**; Number Sense 1.3

Easy Addition Facts

Complete.

Doubles Facts

0
+ 0
□

6
+ 6
□

1
+ 1
□

7
+ 7
□

2
+ 2
□

8
+ 8
□

3
+ 3
□

9
+ 9
□

4
+ 4
□

10
+ 10
□

5
+ 5
□

10 Sums

0
+ □
10

□
+ 4
10

□
+ 9
10

7
+ □
10

□
+ 8
10

□
+ 2
10

3
+ □
10

□
+ 1
10

□
+ 6
10

10
+ □
10

□
+ 5
10

1. Write <, >, or =.

6 ☐ 8

21 ☐ 12

5 + 5 ☐ 10

16 ☐ 4 + 6

2. Tina has Ⓝ Ⓝ Ⓟ Ⓟ Ⓟ Ⓟ.

Fred has Ⓝ Ⓝ Ⓝ Ⓟ Ⓟ Ⓟ.

Who has more money?

_____

How much more money?

_____ ¢

3. How much money?

Ⓝ Ⓓ Ⓝ Ⓟ Ⓓ Ⓝ Ⓝ

_____ ¢

Show this amount with
fewer coins. Use Ⓟ, Ⓝ,
and Ⓓ.

4. Draw the hands.

quarter-past 8 o'clock

1) NS **1.2**   2) NS **2.5**   3) NS 1.5
4) MG 1.2

Date _____

"What's My Rule?"

Find the rules and missing numbers.

1.

in ↓

Rule

out ↓

in	out
7 →	4
11 →	8
4 →	1
9 →	

Your turn: _____ → _____

2.

in ↓

Rule

out ↓

in	out
5 →	10
8 →	13
12 →	17
16 →	

Your turn: _____ → _____

3.

in ↓

Rule

out ↓

in	out
33 →	43
12 →	22
27 →	37
9 →	
24 →	

Your turn: _____ → _____

4.

in ↓

Rule

out ↓

in	out
1 →	2
2 →	4
3 →	6
4 →	
6 →	

Your turn: _____ → _____

LESSON 5·12 Math Boxes

1. Ray has Ⓓ Ⓝ Ⓝ Ⓟ Ⓟ.
Dee has Ⓓ Ⓓ Ⓟ Ⓟ Ⓟ Ⓟ.

Who has more money?

_____

How much more money?

_____ ¢

2. Write the sums.

_____ = [⚄] + [⚄]

[⚃] + [⚅] = _____

_____ = [⚅] + [⚂]

3. What is the temperature?

°F

Choose the best answer.

◯ 60°F   ◯ 72°F

◯ 68°F   ◯ 74°F

4. Count back by 5s.

45, _____, _____,

_____, _____, _____,

_____, _____

1) NS 2.5   2) AF 1.2   3) SDAP 1.0
4) NS 2.4

"What's My Rule?"

Find the rule.

1. in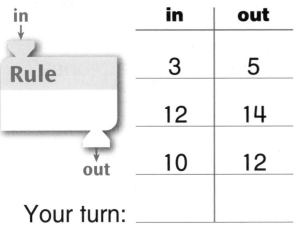

in	out
3	5
12	14
10	12
Your turn:	

2. in

Rule

in	out
4	1
12	9
17	14
Your turn:	

3. What comes out?

in

Rule
+10

out

in	out
3	13
16	
25	
Your turn:	

4. Make your own.

in

Rule

out

in	out

Date _____

1. Write <, >, or =.

28 ⬚ 38

34 ⬚ 43

6 + 7 ⬚ 12

16 ⬚ 10 + 6

2. Lois has Ⓟ Ⓟ Ⓓ Ⓝ Ⓓ Ⓝ.
Joe has Ⓓ Ⓟ Ⓟ Ⓟ Ⓟ Ⓝ.

Who has more money?

_____

How much more money?

_____¢

3. How much money?

Ⓓ Ⓝ Ⓓ Ⓟ Ⓟ Ⓟ Ⓟ Ⓟ Ⓝ

_____¢

Show this amount with
fewer coins. Use Ⓟ, Ⓝ,
and Ⓓ.

4. It is quarter-to _____.

Choose the best answer.

◯ 9 o'clock   ◯ 1 o'clock

◯ 10 o'clock   ◯ 12 o'clock

1) NS 1.2   2) NS 2.5   3) NS 1.5
4) MG 1.2

LESSON 5·14 **Math Boxes**

1. Draw and solve.

Yuko has 3 red balloons, 4 green balloons, and 1 blue balloon.

How many balloons does she have in all?

_____ balloons

2. Draw the hands.

quarter-after 7 o'clock

3. Draw the missing dots.

Find the total number of dots.

$5 + 7 =$ _____

$8 + 3 =$ _____

4. Count up by 5s.

5,   10,   _____,

_____, _____, _____,

_____, _____, _____

Contents

California Projects

PROJECT 9

A Day at the Beach

CALIFORNIA

Measurement and Geometry 2.4; Measurement and Geometry 2.3

People and Objects on the Beach

CALIFORNIA

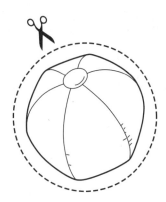

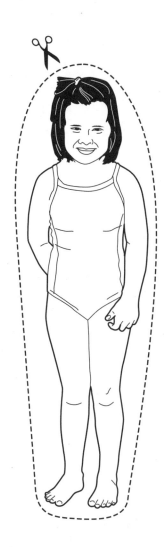

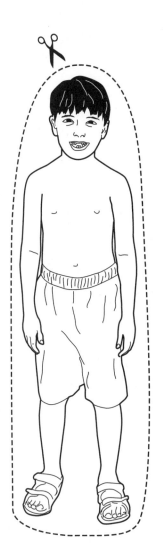

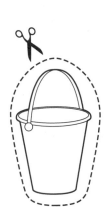

PROJECT 9 — A Day at the Beach Questions

Use your beach scene to complete each sentence.

1. The _____ is next to the _____.

2. The _____ is far from the _____.

3. The _____ is below the _____.

Write two more sentences about your picture.

4. _____

_____

5. _____

_____

Date _____

Write a number story to go with the number sentence.
Then solve.

1. $2 + 3 + 5 =$ _____

_____

_____

2. $4 + 6 + 8 =$ _____

_____

_____

3. $3 + 9 + 1 =$ _____

_____

_____

 Number Sense 2.7; Algebra and Functions 1.3

California Birds

3 California quails

6 greater roadrunners

4 pelicans

9 kingfishers

5 ibises

1 California condor

Date _____

Circle the container that holds **more**.
Underline the container that holds **less**.

1.

2.

Circle the container that holds the **most**.
Underline the container that holds the **least**.

3.

4.

PROJECT 11 **How Long Is It?**

Use paper clips to measure each object.

1.

leaf from an orange tree

about _____ paper clips long

2.

leaf from a lemon tree

about _____ paper clips long

3. Choose a small object. Use paper clips to measure the object. Draw a picture of the object you measured.

about _____ paper clips long

California Content Standards

The California Mathematics Content Standards describe what every child in California can and needs to learn in mathematics. These standards are identified at the bottom of each of your journal pages and are listed here for your reference. The oval identifies the key standards for this grade level.

Number Sense

Number Sense 1.0 Students understand and use numbers up to 100:

Number Sense 1.1 Count, read, and write whole numbers to 100.

Number Sense 1.2 Compare and order whole numbers to 100 by using the symbols for less than, equal to, or greater than (<, =, >).

Number Sense 1.3 Represent equivalent forms of the same number through the use of physical models, diagrams, and number expressions (to 20) (e.g., 8 may be represented as 4 + 4, 5 + 3, 2 + 2 + 2 + 2, 10 − 2, 11 − 3).

Number Sense 1.4 Count and group objects in ones and tens (e.g., three groups of 10 and 4 equals 34, or 30 + 4).

Number Sense 1.5 Identify and know the value of coins and show different combinations of coins that equal the same value.

Number Sense 2.0 Students demonstrate the meaning of addition and subtraction and use these operations to solve problems:

Number Sense 2.1 Know the addition facts (sums to 20) and the corresponding subtraction facts and commit them to memory.

Number Sense 2.2 Use the inverse relationship between addition and subtraction to solve problems.

Number Sense 2.3 Identify one more than, one less than, 10 more than, and 10 less than a given number.

Number Sense 2.4 Count by 2s, 5s, and 10s to 100.

Number Sense 2.5 Show the meaning of addition (putting together, increasing) and subtraction (taking away, comparing, finding the difference).

Number Sense 2.6 Solve addition and subtraction problems with one- and two-digit numbers (e.g., 5 + 58 = __).

Number Sense 2.7 Find the sum of three one-digit numbers.

Number Sense 3.0 Students use estimation strategies in computation and problem solving that involve numbers that use the ones, tens, and hundreds places:

Number Sense 3.1 Make reasonable estimates when comparing larger or smaller numbers.

Algebra and Functions

Algebra and Functions 1.0 Students use number sentences with operational symbols and expressions to solve problems:

Algebra and Functions 1.1 Write and solve number sentences from problem situations that express relationships involving addition and subtraction.

Algebra and Functions 1.2 Understand the meaning of the symbols +, −, =.

Algebra and Functions 1.3 Create problem situations that might lead to given number sentences involving addition and subtraction.

Measurement and Geometry

Measurement and Geometry 1.0 Students use direct comparison and nonstandard units to describe the measurement of objects:

Measurement and Geometry 1.1 Compare the length, weight, and volume of two or more objects by using direct comparison or a nonstandard unit.

Measurement and Geometry 1.2 Tell time to the nearest half hour and relate time to events (e.g., before/after, shorter/longer).

Measurement and Geometry 2.0 Students identify common geometric figures, classify them by common attributes, and describe their relative position or their location in space:

Measurement and Geometry 2.1 Identify, describe, and compare triangles, rectangles, squares, and circles, including the faces of three-dimensional objects.

Measurement and Geometry 2.2 Classify familiar plane and solid objects by common attributes, such as color, position, shape, size, roundness, or number of corners, and explain which attributes are being used for classification.

Measurement and Geometry 2.3 Give and follow directions about location.

Measurement and Geometry 2.4 Arrange and describe objects in space by proximity, position, and direction (e.g., near, far, below, above, up, down, behind, in front of, next to, left or right of).

Statistics, Data Analysis, and Probability

Statistics, Data Analysis, and Probability 1.0 Students organize, represent, and compare data by category on simple graphs and charts:

Statistics, Data Analysis, and Probability 1.1 Sort objects and data by common attributes and describe the categories.

Statistics, Data Analysis, and Probability 1.2 Represent and compare data (e.g., largest, smallest, most often, least often) by using pictures, bar graphs, tally charts, and picture graphs.

Statistics, Data Analysis, and Probability 2.0 Students sort objects and create and describe patterns by numbers, shapes, sizes, rhythms, or colors:

Statistics, Data Analysis, and Probability 2.1 Describe, extend, and explain ways to get to a next element in simple repeating patterns (e.g., rhythmic, numeric, color, and shape).

Mathematical Reasoning

Mathematical Reasoning 1.0 Students make decisions about how to set up a problem:

Mathematical Reasoning 1.1 Determine the approach, materials, and strategies to be used.

Mathematical Reasoning 1.2 Use tools, such as manipulatives or sketches, to model problems.

Mathematical Reasoning 2.0 Students solve problems and justify their reasoning:

Mathematical Reasoning 2.1 Explain the reasoning used and justify the procedures selected.

Mathematical Reasoning 2.2 Make precise calculations and check the validity of the results in the context of the problem.

Mathematical Reasoning 3.0 Students note connections between one problem and another.

California Content Standards for Math Boxes

Math Boxes 2◆3

1. **Number Sense 1.1** Count, read, and write whole numbers to 100.
2. **Number Sense 2.4** Count by 2s, 5s, and 10s to 100.
3. **Number Sense 2.3** Identify one more than, one less than, 10 more than, and 10 less than a given number.
4. **Number Sense 1.0** Students understand and use numbers up to 100.

Math Boxes 2◆4

1. **Number Sense 1.0** Students understand and use numbers up to 100.
2. **Statistics, Data Analysis, and Probability 1.0** Students organize, represent, and compare data by category on simple graphs and charts.
3. **Number Sense 1.3** Represent equivalent forms of the same number through the use of physical models, diagrams, and number expressions (to 20) (e.g., 8 may be represented as $4 + 4$, $5 + 3$, $2 + 2 + 2 + 2$, $10 − 2$, $11 − 3$).
4. **Number Sense 1.1** Count, read, and write whole numbers to 100.

Math Boxes 2◆5

1. **Number Sense 1.1** Count, read, and write whole numbers to 100.
2. **Number Sense 2.4** Count by 2s, 5s, and 10s to 100.
3. **Number Sense 2.3** Identify one more than, one less than, 10 more than, and 10 less than a given number.
4. **Number Sense 1.0** Students understand and use numbers up to 100.

Math Boxes 2◆6

1. **Number Sense 1.0** Students understand and use numbers up to 100.
2. **Statistics, Data Analysis, and Probability 1.0** Students organize, represent, and compare data by category on simple graphs and charts.
3. **Number Sense 1.3** Represent equivalent forms of the same number through the use of physical models, diagrams, and number expressions (to 20) (e.g., 8 may be represented as $4 + 4$, $5 + 3$, $2 + 2 + 2 + 2$, $10 − 2$, $11 − 3$).
4. **Number Sense 1.1** Count, read, and write whole numbers to 100.
5. **Measurement and Geometry 1.2** Tell time to the nearest half hour and relate time to events (e.g., before/after, shorter/longer).

Math Boxes 2◆7

1. **Measurement and Geometry 1.2** Tell time to the nearest half hour and relate time to events (e.g., before/after, shorter/longer).
2. **Number Sense 2.0** Students demonstrate the meaning of addition and subtraction and use these operations to solve problems.
3. **Number Sense 1.2** Compare and order whole numbers to 100 by using the symbols for less than, equal to, or greater than ($<, =, >$).
4. **Measurement and Geometry 1.2** Tell time to the nearest half hour and relate time to events (e.g., before/after, shorter/longer).

Math Boxes 2◆8

1. **Number Sense 2.0** Students demonstrate the meaning of addition and subtraction and use these operations to solve problems.
2. **Number Sense 1.5** Identify and know the value of coins and show different combinations of coins that equal the same value.
3. **Statistics, Data Analysis, and Probability 2.1** Describe, extend, and explain ways to get to a next element in simple repeating patterns (e.g., rhythmic, numeric, color, and shape).
4. **Number Sense 2.4** Count by 2s, 5s, and 10s to 100.

Math Boxes 2◆9

1. **Measurement and Geometry 1.2** Tell time to the nearest half hour and relate time to events (e.g., before/after, shorter/longer).
2. **Number Sense 2.0** Students demonstrate the meaning of addition and subtraction and use these operations to solve problems.
3. **Number Sense 1.2** Compare and order whole numbers to 100 by using the symbols for less than, equal to, or greater than ($<, =, >$).
4. **Measurement and Geometry 1.2** Tell time to the nearest half hour and relate time to events (e.g., before/after, shorter/longer).

Math Boxes 2◆10

1. **Number Sense 2.0** Students demonstrate the meaning of addition and subtraction and use these operations to solve problems.
2. **Number Sense 1.5** Identify and know the value of coins and show different combinations of coins that equal the same value.
3. **Statistics, Data Analysis, and Probability 2.1** Describe, extend, and explain ways to get to a next element in simple repeating patterns (e.g., rhythmic, numeric, color, and shape).
4. **Number Sense 2.4** Count by 2s, 5s, and 10s to 100.

Math Boxes 2◆11

1. **Number Sense 1.5** Identify and know the value of coins and show different combinations of coins that equal the same value.
2. **Measurement and Geometry 1.2** Tell time to the nearest half hour and relate time to events (e.g., before/after, shorter/longer).

Math Boxes 2•11 cont.

3. Statistics, Data Analysis, and Probability 1.2 Represent and compare data (e.g., largest, smallest, most often, least often) by using pictures, bar graphs, tally charts, and picture graphs.

4. Number Sense 2.4 Count by 2s, 5s, and 10s to 100.

Math Boxes 2•12

1. Number Sense 2.0 Students demonstrate the meaning of addition and subtraction and use these operations to solve problems.

2. Number Sense 1.5 Identify and know the value of coins and show different combinations of coins that equal the same value.

3. Statistics, Data Analysis, and Probability 2.1 Describe, extend, and explain ways to get to a next element in simple repeating patterns (e.g., rhythmic, numeric, color, and shape).

4. Number Sense 2.4 Count by 2s, 5s, and 10s to 100.

Math Boxes 2•13

1. Number Sense 1.5 Identify and know the value of coins and show different combinations of coins that equal the same value.

2. Measurement and Geometry 1.2 Tell time to the nearest half hour and relate time to events (e.g., before/after, shorter/longer).

3. Statistics, Data Analysis, and Probability 1.2 Represent and compare data (e.g., largest, smallest, most often, least often) by using pictures, bar graphs, tally charts, and picture graphs.

4. Number Sense 2.4 Count by 2s, 5s, and 10s to 100.

Math Boxes 2•14

1. Number Sense 1.0 Students understand and use numbers up to 100.

2. Number Sense 2.4 Count by 2s, 5s, and 10s to 100.

3. Statistics, Data Analysis, and Probability 2.0 Students sort objects and create and describe patterns by numbers, shapes, sizes, rhythms, or colors.

4. Number Sense 1.1 Count, read, and write whole numbers to 100.

Math Boxes 3•1

1. Number Sense 1.0 Students understand and use numbers up to 100.

2. Measurement and Geometry 1.2 Tell time to the nearest half hour and relate time to events (e.g., before/after, shorter/longer).

3. Number Sense 1.5 Identify and know the value of coins and show different combinations of coins that equal the same value.

4. Statistics, Data Analysis, and Probability 1.0 Students organize, represent, and compare data by category on simple graphs and charts.

Math Boxes 3•2

1. Number Sense 1.5 Identify and know the value of coins and show different combinations of coins that equal the same value.

2. Statistics, Data Analysis, and Probability 1.2 Represent and compare data (e.g., largest, smallest, most often, least often) by using pictures, bar graphs, tally charts, and picture graphs.

3. Number Sense 1.3 Represent equivalent forms of the same number through the use of physical models, diagrams, and number expressions (to 20) (e.g., 8 may be represented as $4 + 4$, $5 + 3$, $2 + 2 + 2 + 2$, $10 - 2$, $11 - 3$).

4. Number Sense 2.3 Identify one more than, one less than, 10 more than, and 10 less than a given number.

Math Boxes 3•3

1. Number Sense 1.0 Students understand and use numbers up to 100.

2. Measurement and Geometry 1.2 Tell time to the nearest half hour and relate time to events (e.g., before/after, shorter/longer).

3. Number Sense 1.5 Identify and know the value of coins and show different combinations of coins that equal the same value.

4. Statistics, Data Analysis, and Probability 1.0 Students organize, represent, and compare data by category on simple graphs and charts.

Math Boxes 3•4

1. Number Sense 1.5 Identify and know the value of coins and show different combinations of coins that equal the same value.

2. Statistics, Data Analysis, and Probability 1.2 Represent and compare data (e.g., largest, smallest, most often, least often) by using pictures, bar graphs, tally charts, and picture graphs.

3. Number Sense 1.3 Represent equivalent forms of the same number through the use of physical models, diagrams, and number expressions (to 20) (e.g., 8 may be represented as $4 + 4$, $5 + 3$, $2 + 2 + 2 + 2$, $10 - 2$, $11 - 3$).

4. Number Sense 2.3 Identify one more than, one less than, 10 more than, and 10 less than a given number.

Math Boxes 3•5

1. Statistics, Data Analysis, and Probability 1.2 Represent and compare data (e.g., largest, smallest, most often, least often) by using pictures, bar graphs, tally charts, and picture graphs.

2. Number Sense 2.4 Count by 2s, 5s, and 10s to 100.

3. Number Sense 1.0 Students understand and use numbers up to 100.

4. Number Sense 1.1 Count, read, and write whole numbers to 100.

Math Boxes 3•6

1. Number Sense 2.3 Identify one more than, one less than, 10 more than, and 10 less than a given number.

CA14

Math Boxes 3∙6 *cont.*

2. Measurement and Geometry 1.2 Tell time to the nearest half hour and relate time to events (e.g., before/after, shorter/longer).

3. Number Sense 2.4 Count by 2s, 5s, and 10s to 100.

4. Measurement and Geometry 1.1 Compare the length, weight, and volume of two or more objects by using direct comparison or a nonstandard unit.

Math Boxes 3∙7

1. Statistics, Data Analysis, and Probability 1.2 Represent and compare data (e.g., largest, smallest, most often, least often) by using pictures, bar graphs, tally charts, and picture graphs.

2. Number Sense 2.4 Count by 2s, 5s, and 10s to 100.

3. Number Sense 1.0 Students understand and use numbers up to 100.

4. Number Sense 1.3 Represent equivalent forms of the same number through the use of physical models, diagrams, and number expressions (to 20) (e.g., 8 may be represented as $4 + 4$, $5 + 3$, $2 + 2 + 2 + 2$, $10 - 2$, $11 - 3$).

Math Boxes 3∙8

1. Number Sense 2.3 Identify one more than, one less than, 10 more than, and 10 less than a given number.

2. Measurement and Geometry 1.2 Tell time to the nearest half hour and relate time to events (e.g., before/after, shorter/longer).

3. Number Sense 2.4 Count by 2s, 5s, and 10s to 100.

4. Measurement and Geometry 1.1 Compare the length, weight, and volume of two or more objects by using direct comparison or a nonstandard unit.

Math Boxes 3∙9

1. Number Sense 2.1 Know the addition facts (sums to 20) and the corresponding subtraction facts and commit them to memory.

2. Measurement and Geometry 1.2 Tell time to the nearest half hour and relate time to events (e.g., before/after, shorter/longer).

3. Statistics, Data Analysis, and Probability 2.1 Describe, extend, and explain ways to get to a next element in simple repeating patterns (e.g., rhythmic, numeric, color, and shape).

4. Number Sense 2.4 Count by 2s, 5s, and 10s to 100.

Math Boxes 3∙10

1. Number Sense 1.0 Students understand and use numbers up to 100.

2. Number Sense 1.3 Represent equivalent forms of the same number through the use of physical models, diagrams, and number expressions (to 20) (e.g., 8 may be represented as $4 + 4$, $5 + 3$, $2 + 2 + 2 + 2$, $10 - 2$, $11 - 3$).

3. Statistics, Data Analysis, and Probability 2.1 Describe, extend, and explain ways to get to a next element in simple repeating patterns (e.g., rhythmic, numeric, color, and shape).

4. Algebra and Functions 1.0 Students use number sentences with operational symbols and expressions to solve problems.

Math Boxes 3∙11

1. Number Sense 2.1 Know the addition facts (sums to 20) and the corresponding subtraction facts and commit them to memory.

2. Measurement and Geometry 1.2 Tell time to the nearest half hour and relate time to events (e.g., before/after, shorter/longer).

3. Statistics, Data Analysis, and Probability 2.1 Describe, extend, and explain ways to get to a next element in simple repeating patterns (e.g., rhythmic, numeric, color, and shape).

4. Number Sense 2.4 Count by 2s, 5s, and 10s to 100.

Math Boxes 3∙12

1. Number Sense 2.1 Know the addition facts (sums to 20) and the corresponding subtraction facts and commit them to memory.

2. Measurement and Geometry 1.2 Tell time to the nearest half hour and relate time to events (e.g., before/after, shorter/longer).

3. Number Sense 1.5 Identify and know the value of coins and show different combinations of coins that equal the same value.

4. Algebra and Functions 1.1 Write and solve number sentences from problem situations that express relationships involving addition and subtraction.

Math Boxes 3∙13

1. Number Sense 1.0 Students understand and use numbers up to 100.

2. Number Sense 1.3 Represent equivalent forms of the same number through the use of physical models, diagrams, and number expressions (to 20) (e.g., 8 may be represented as $4 + 4$, $5 + 3$, $2 + 2 + 2 + 2$, $10 - 2$, $11 - 3$).

3. Statistics, Data Analysis, and Probability 2.1 Describe, extend, and explain ways to get to a next element in simple repeating patterns (e.g., rhythmic, numeric, color, and shape).

4. Algebra and Functions 1.0 Students use number sentences with operational symbols and expressions to solve problems.

Math Boxes 3∙14

1. Number Sense 2.1 Know the addition facts (sums to 20) and the corresponding subtraction facts and commit them to memory.

2. Measurement and Geometry 1.2 Tell time to the nearest half hour and relate time to events (e.g., before/after, shorter/longer).

3. Number Sense 1.5 Identify and know the value of coins and show different combinations of coins that equal the same value.

Math Boxes 3•14 *cont.*

4. Algebra and Functions 1.1 Write and solve number sentences from problem situations that express relationships involving addition and subtraction.

Math Boxes 3•15

1. Statistics, Data Analysis, and Probability 1.0 Students organize, represent, and compare data by category on simple graphs and charts.

2. Measurement and Geometry 1.1 Compare the length, weight, and volume of two or more objects by using direct comparison or a nonstandard unit.

3. Number Sense (2.3) Identify one more than, one less than, 10 more than, and 10 less than a given number.

4. Number Sense (2.4) Count by 2s, 5s, and 10s to 100.

Math Boxes 4•1

1. Number Sense 1.0 Students understand and use numbers up to 100.

2. Statistics, Data Analysis, and Probability (2.1) Describe, extend, and explain ways to get to a next element in simple repeating patterns (e.g., rhythmic, numeric, color, and shape).

3. Number Sense (2.1) Know the addition facts (sums to 20) and the corresponding subtraction facts and commit them to memory.

4. Number Sense 1.0 Students understand and use numbers up to 100.

Math Boxes 4•2

1. Statistics, Data Analysis, and Probability 1.0 Students organize, represent, and compare data by category on simple graphs and charts.

2. Statistics, Data Analysis, and Probability (2.1) Describe, extend, and explain ways to get to a next element in simple repeating patterns (e.g., rhythmic, numeric, color, and shape).

3. Number Sense (2.3) Identify one more than, one less than, 10 more than, and 10 less than a given number.

4. Number Sense (2.4) Count by 2s, 5s, and 10s to 100.

Math Boxes 4•3

1. Number Sense 1.0 Students understand and use numbers up to 100.

2. Statistics, Data Analysis, and Probability (2.1) Describe, extend, and explain ways to get to a next element in simple repeating patterns (e.g., rhythmic, numeric, color, and shape).

3. Number Sense (2.1) Know the addition facts (sums to 20) and the corresponding subtraction facts and commit them to memory.

4. Number Sense 1.0 Students understand and use numbers up to 100.

Math Boxes 4•4

1. Statistics, Data Analysis, and Probability 1.0 Students organize, represent, and compare data by category on simple graphs and charts.

2. Statistics, Data Analysis, and Probability (2.1) Describe, extend, and explain ways to get to a next element in simple repeating patterns (e.g., rhythmic, numeric, color, and shape).

3. Number Sense (2.3) Identify one more than, one less than, 10 more than, and 10 less than a given number.

4. Number Sense (2.4) Count by 2s, 5s, and 10s to 100.

Math Boxes 4•5

1. Measurement and Geometry 1.0 Students use direct comparison and nonstandard units to describe the measurements of objects.

2. Statistics, Data Analysis, and Probability 1.2 Represent and compare data (e.g., largest, smallest, most often, least often) by using pictures, bar graphs, tally charts, and picture graphs.

3. Number Sense (2.4) Count by 2s, 5s, and 10s to 100.

4. Algebra and Functions 1.2 Understand the meaning of the symbols $+, -, =$.

Math Boxes 4•6

1. Measurement and Geometry 1.0 Students use direct comparison and nonstandard units to describe the measurements of objects.

2. Number Sense 1.5 Identify and know the value of coins and show different combinations of coins that equal the same value.

3. Number Sense (2.5) Show the meaning of addition (putting together, increasing) and subtraction (taking away, comparing, finding the difference).

4. Number Sense 1.5 Identify and know the value of coins and show different combinations of coins that equal the same value.

Math Boxes 4•7

1. Measurement and Geometry 1.0 Students use direct comparison and nonstandard units to describe the measurements of objects.

2. Statistics, Data Analysis, and Probability 1.2 Represent and compare data (e.g., largest, smallest, most often, least often) by using pictures, bar graphs, tally charts, and picture graphs.

3. Number Sense (2.4) Count by 2s, 5s, and 10s to 100.

4. Algebra and Functions 1.2 Understand the meaning of the symbols $+, -, =$.

Math Boxes 4•8

1. Measurement and Geometry 1.0 Students use direct comparison and nonstandard units to describe the measurements of objects.

2. Number Sense 1.5 Identify and know the value of coins and show different combinations of coins that equal the same value.

CA16

Math Boxes 4•8 *cont.*

3. Number Sense **2.5** Show the meaning of addition (putting together, increasing) and subtraction (taking away, comparing, finding the difference).

4. Number Sense 1.5 Identify and know the value of coins and show different combinations of coins that equal the same value.

Math Boxes 4•9

1. Measurement and Geometry 1.0 Students use direct comparison and nonstandard units to describe the measurements of objects.

2. Measurement and Geometry 1.2 Tell time to the nearest half hour and relate time to events (e.g., before/after, shorter/longer).

3. Number Sense **2.1** Know the addition facts (sums to 20) and the corresponding subtraction facts and commit them to memory.

4. Algebra and Functions 1.0 Students use number sentences with operational symbols and expressions to solve problems.

Math Boxes 4•10

1. Mathematical Reasoning 2.0 Students solve problems and justify their reasoning.

2. Statistics, Data Analysis, and Probability **2.1** Describe, extend, and explain ways to get to a next element in simple repeating patterns (e.g., rhythmic, numeric, color, and shape).

3. Number Sense **2.1** Know the addition facts (sums to 20) and the corresponding subtraction facts and commit them to memory.

4. Algebra and Functions 1.0 Students use number sentences with operational symbols and expressions to solve problems.

Math Boxes 4•11

1. Measurement and Geometry 1.0 Students use direct comparison and nonstandard units to describe the measurements of objects.

2. Measurement and Geometry 1.2 Tell time to the nearest half hour and relate time to events (e.g., before/after, shorter/longer).

3. Number Sense **2.1** Know the addition facts (sums to 20) and the corresponding subtraction facts and commit them to memory.

4. Algebra and Functions 1.0 Students use number sentences with operational symbols and expressions to solve problems.

Math Boxes 4•12

1. Mathematical Reasoning 2.0 Students solve problems and justify their reasoning.

2. Statistics, Data Analysis, and Probability **2.1** Describe, extend, and explain ways to get to a next element in simple repeating patterns (e.g., rhythmic, numeric, color, and shape).

3. Number Sense **2.1** Know the addition facts (sums to 20) and the corresponding subtraction facts and commit them to memory.

4. Algebra and Functions 1.0 Students use number sentences with operational symbols and expressions to solve problems.

Math Boxes 4•13

1. Number Sense 1.0 Students understand and use numbers up to 100.

2. Number Sense **2.5** Show the meaning of addition (putting together, increasing) and subtraction (taking away, comparing, finding the difference).

3. Algebra and Functions 1.2 Understand the meaning of the symbols $+, -, =$.

4. Number Sense 1.3 Represent equivalent forms of the same number through the use of physical models, diagrams, and number expressions (to 20) (e.g., 8 may be represented as $4 + 4$, $5 + 3$, $2 + 2 + 2 + 2$, $10 - 2$, $11 - 3$).

Math Boxes 5•1

1. Number Sense 1.4 Count and group objects in ones and tens (e.g., three groups of 10 and 4 equals 34, or $30 + 4$).

2. Statistics, Data Analysis, and Probability **2.1** Describe, extend, and explain ways to get to a next element in simple repeating patterns (e.g., rhythmic, numeric, color, and shape).

3. Algebra and Functions 1.0 Students use number sentences with operational symbols and expressions to solve problems.

4. Number Sense 1.0 Students understand and use numbers up to 100.

Math Boxes 5•2

1. Number Sense 1.4 Count and group objects in ones and tens (e.g., three groups of 10 and 4 equals 34, or $30 + 4$).

2. Number Sense 1.3 Represent equivalent forms of the same number through the use of physical models, diagrams, and number expressions (to 20) (e.g., 8 may be represented as $4 + 4$, $5 + 3$, $2 + 2 + 2 + 2$, $10 - 2$, $11 - 3$).

3. Number Sense 2.6 Solve addition and subtraction problems with one- and two-digit numbers (e.g., $5 + 58 =$ __).

4. Number Sense **2.5** Show the meaning of addition (putting together, increasing) and subtraction (taking away, comparing, finding the difference).

Math Boxes 5•3

1. Number Sense 1.4 Count and group objects in ones and tens (e.g., three groups of 10 and 4 equals 34, or $30 + 4$).

2. Statistics, Data Analysis, and Probability **2.1** Describe, extend, and explain ways to get to a next element in simple repeating patterns (e.g., rhythmic, numeric, color, and shape).

3. Algebra and Functions 1.0 Students use number sentences with operational symbols and expressions to solve problems.

4. Number Sense 1.0 Students understand and use numbers up to 100.

Math Boxes 5•4

1. Number Sense 1.4 Count and group objects in ones and tens (e.g., three groups of 10 and 4 equals 34, or $30 + 4$).

2. Number Sense 1.3 Represent equivalent forms of the same number through the use of physical models, diagrams, and number expressions (to 20) (e.g., 8 may be represented as $4 + 4$, $5 + 3$, $2 + 2 + 2 + 2$, $10 - 2$, $11 - 3$).

Math Boxes 5·4 *cont.*

3. **Number Sense 2.6** Solve addition and subtraction problems with one- and two-digit numbers (e.g., $5 + 58 =$ __).

4. **Number Sense 2.5** Show the meaning of addition (putting together, increasing) and subtraction (taking away, comparing, finding the difference).

Math Boxes 5·5

1. **Number Sense 1.4** Count and group objects in ones and tens (e.g., three groups of 10 and 4 equals 34, or $30 + 4$).

2. **Number Sense 2.6** Solve addition and subtraction problems with one- and two-digit numbers (e.g., $5 + 58 =$ __).

3. **Measurement and Geometry 1.0** Students use direct comparison and nonstandard units to describe the measurements of objects.

4. **Algebra and Functions 1.1** Write and solve number sentences from problem situations that express relationships involving addition and subtraction.

Math Boxes 5·6

1. **Statistics, Data Analysis, and Probability 2.1** Describe, extend, and explain ways to get to a next element in simple repeating patterns (e.g., rhythmic, numeric, color, and shape).

2. **Number Sense 1.5** Identify and know the value of coins and show different combinations of coins that equal the same value.

3. **Statistics, Data Analysis, and Probability 1.2** Represent and compare data (e.g., largest, smallest, most often, least often) by using pictures, bar graphs, tally charts, and picture graphs.

4. **Number Sense 2.5** Show the meaning of addition (putting together, increasing) and subtraction (taking away, comparing, finding the difference).

Math Boxes 5·7

1. **Number Sense 1.4** Count and group objects in ones and tens (e.g., three groups of 10 and 4 equals 34, or $30 + 4$).

2. **Number Sense 2.6** Solve addition and subtraction problems with one- and two-digit numbers (e.g., $5 + 58 =$ __).

3. **Measurement and Geometry 1.0** Students use direct comparison and nonstandard units to describe the measurements of objects.

4. **Algebra and Functions 1.1** Write and solve number sentences from problem situations that express relationships involving addition and subtraction.

Math Boxes 5·8

1. **Statistics, Data Analysis, and Probability 2.1** Describe, extend, and explain ways to get to a next element in simple repeating patterns (e.g., rhythmic, numeric, color, and shape).

2. **Number Sense 1.5** Identify and know the value of coins and show different combinations of coins that equal the same value.

3. **Statistics, Data Analysis, and Probability 1.2** Represent and compare data (e.g., largest, smallest, most often, least often) by using pictures, bar graphs, tally charts, and picture graphs.

4. **Number Sense 2.5** Show the meaning of addition (putting together, increasing) and subtraction (taking away, comparing, finding the difference).

Math Boxes 5·9

1. **Number Sense 1.2** Compare and order whole numbers to 100 by using the symbols for less than, equal to, or greater than ($<, =, >$).

2. **Number Sense 2.5** Show the meaning of addition (putting together, increasing) and subtraction (taking away, comparing, finding the difference).

3. **Number Sense 1.5** Identify and know the value of coins and show different combinations of coins that equal the same value.

4. **Measurement and Geometry 1.2** Tell time to the nearest half hour and relate time to events (e.g., before/after, shorter/longer).

Math Boxes 5·10

1. **Number Sense 2.5** Show the meaning of addition (putting together, increasing) and subtraction (taking away, comparing, finding the difference).

2. **Algebra and Functions 1.2** Understand the meaning of the symbols $+, -, =$.

3. **Statistics, Data Analysis, and Probability 1.0** Students organize, represent, and compare data by category on simple graphs and charts.

4. **Number Sense 2.4** Count by 2s, 5s, and 10s to 100.

Math Boxes 5·11

1. **Number Sense 1.2** Compare and order whole numbers to 100 by using the symbols for less than, equal to, or greater than ($<, =, >$).

2. **Number Sense 2.5** Show the meaning of addition (putting together, increasing) and subtraction (taking away, comparing, finding the difference).

3. **Number Sense 1.5** Identify and know the value of coins and show different combinations of coins that equal the same value.

4. **Measurement and Geometry 1.2** Tell time to the nearest half hour and relate time to events (e.g., before/after, shorter/longer).

Math Boxes 5·12

1. **Number Sense 2.5** Show the meaning of addition (putting together, increasing) and subtraction (taking away, comparing, finding the difference).

2. **Algebra and Functions 1.2** Understand the meaning of the symbols $+, -, =$.

3. **Statistics, Data Analysis, and Probability 1.0** Students organize, represent, and compare data by category on simple graphs and charts.

4. **Number Sense 2.4** Count by 2s, 5s, and 10s to 100.

Math Boxes 5·13

1. **Number Sense 1.2** Compare and order whole numbers to 100 by using the symbols for less than, equal to, or greater than ($<, =, >$).

2. **Number Sense 2.5** Show the meaning of addition (putting together, increasing) and subtraction (taking away, comparing, finding the difference).

3. **Number Sense 1.5** Identify and know the value of coins and show different combinations of coins that equal the same value.

Math Boxes 5✦13 *cont.*

4. **Measurement and Geometry 1.2** Tell time to the nearest half hour and relate time to events (e.g., before/after, shorter/longer).

Math Boxes 5✦14

1. **Number Sense 2.7** Find the sum of three one-digit numbers.

2. **Measurement and Geometry 1.2** Tell time to the nearest half hour and relate time to events (e.g., before/after, shorter/longer).

3. **Algebra and Functions 1.1** Write and solve number sentences from problem situations that express relationships involving addition and subtraction.

4. **Number Sense 2.4** Count by 2s, 5s, and 10s to 100.

Number Cards 0–15

15	**14**	**13**	**12**
11	**10**	**9**	**8**
7	**6**	**5**	**4**
3	**2**	**1**	**0**

Number Cards

Number Cards 16–22

16	**17**	**18**	**19**
20	**21**	**22**	**+**
—	**✕**	**÷**	**=**
<	**?**	**wild card**	**wild card**

Number Cards 0–9

1   0

5   4   3   2

9   8   7   6

Name _____   **Date** _____

Clock Face, Hour and Minute

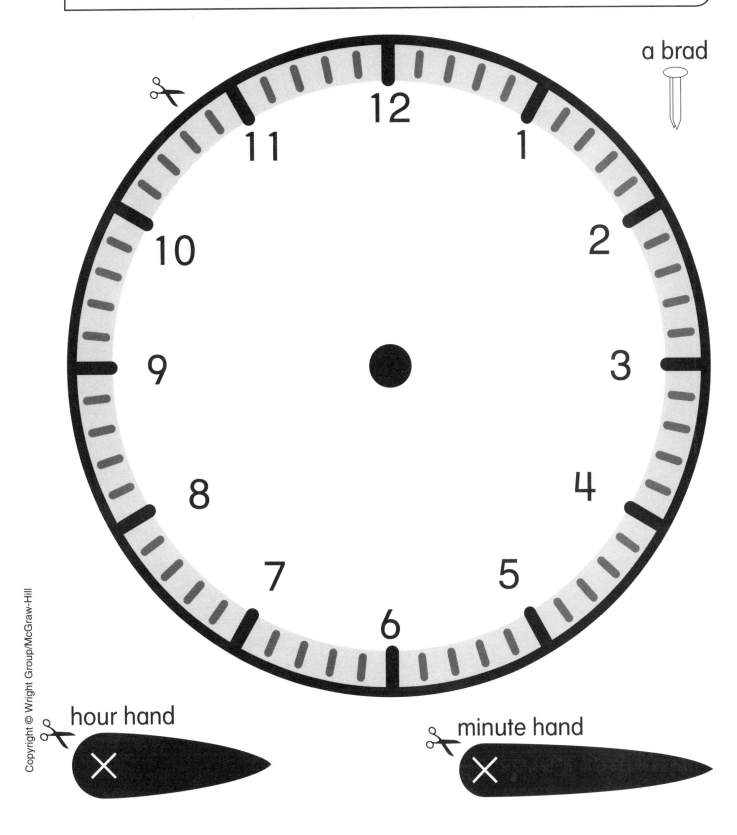

a brad

hour hand

minute hand

Activity Sheet 3

Domino Cutouts

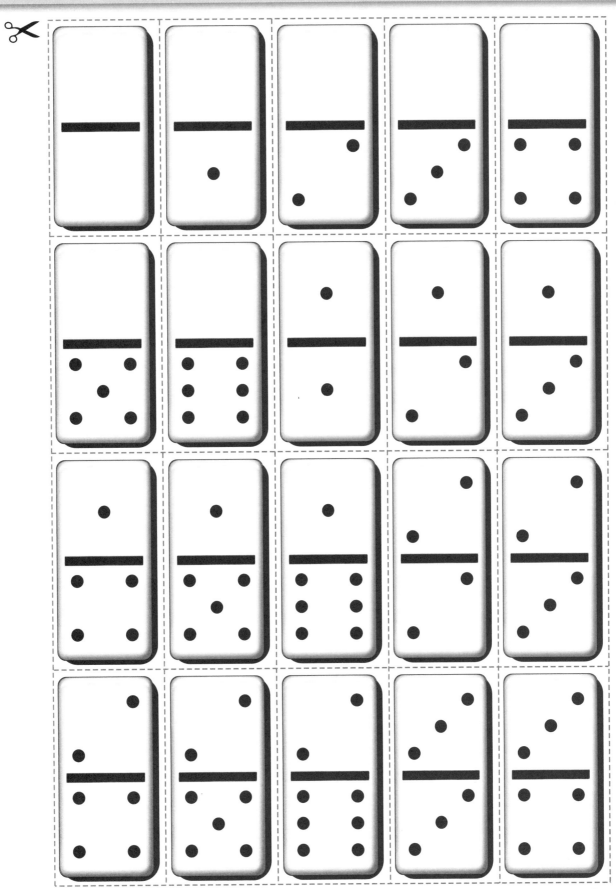

Domino Cutouts

✂

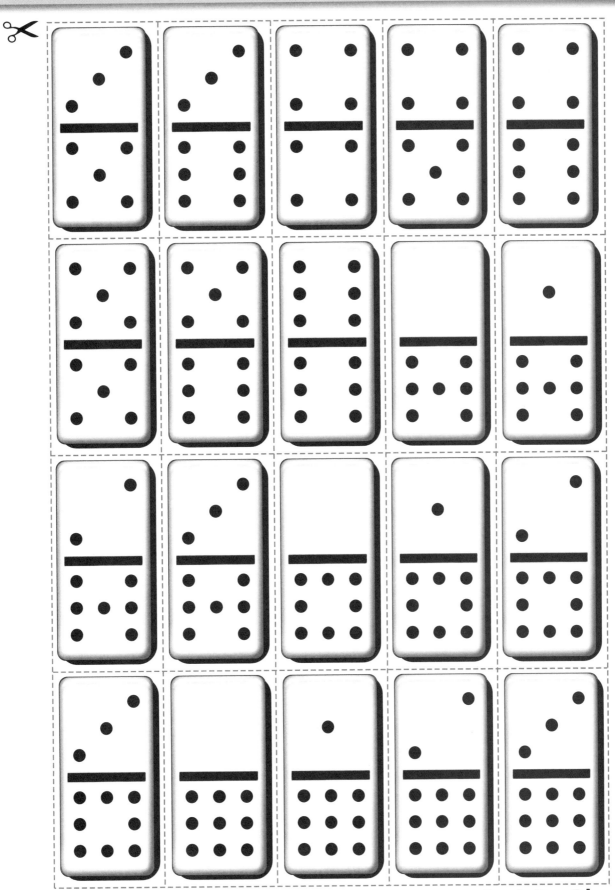

Place-Value Mat

	Hundreds
	Tens
	Ones

Animal Cards

First-grade girl
41 lb

7-year-old boy
50 lb

Cheetah
120 lb

Porpoise
98 lb

Penguin
75 lb

Beaver
56 lb

Activity Sheet 7

Animal Cards

7-year-old boy
50 in.

First-grade girl
43 in.

Porpoise
72 in.

Cheetah
48 in.

Beaver
30 in.

Penguin
36 in.

Activity Sheet 7

Animal Cards

Cat
7 lb

Fox
14 lb

Koala
19 lb

Raccoon
23 lb

Rabbit
6 lb

Eagle
15 lb

Activity Sheet 8

Animal Cards

Fox

20 in.

Cat

12 in.

Raccoon

23 in.

Koala

24 in.

Eagle

35 in.

Rabbit

11 in.

Activity Sheet 8